W9-BQU-112

HEATH
MIDDLE LEVEL
LITERATURE

Changes and Choices

Moving from adolescence to adulthood involves exciting
and challenging changes and choices. What will you make
of life's challenges?

AUTHORS

Donna Alvermann
Linda Miller Cleary
Kenneth Donelson
Donald Gallo
Alice Haskins
J. Howard Johnston
John Lounsbury
Alleen Pace Nilsen
Robert Pavlik
Jewell Parker Rhodes
Alberto Alvaro Ríos
Sandra Schurr
Lyndon Searfoss
Julia Thomason
Max Thompson
Carl Zon

D.C. Heath and Company
Lexington, Massachusetts / Toronto, Ontario

STAFF CREDITS

EDITORIAL   Barbara A. Brennan, Susan Belt Cogley, DeVona Dors, Christopher Johnson, Rita M. Sullivan, Patricia B. Weiler

Proofreading: JoAnne B. Sgroi

CONTRIBUTING WRITERS   Kathy Tuchman Glass, Jo Pitkin

SERIES DESIGN   Robin Herr

BOOK DESIGN   Caroline Bowden, Daniel Derdula, Susan Geer, Diana Maloney, Angela Sciaraffa, Bonnie Chayes Yousefian

Art Editing: Carolyn Langley

PHOTOGRAPHY   *Series Photography Coordinator:* Carmen Johnson

Photo Research Supervisor: Martha Friedman

Photo Researchers: Wendy Enright, Linda Finigan, Po-yee McKenna, PhotoSearch, Inc., Gillian Speeth, Denise Theodores

Assignment Photography Coordinators: Susan Doheny, Gayna Hoffman, Shawna Johnston

COMPUTER PREPRESS   Ricki Pappo, Kathy Meisl, Richard Curran, Michele Locatelli

PERMISSIONS   Dorothy B. McLeod

PRODUCTION   Patrick Connolly

Cover *collage photos* Top row 1. John Owens/©D.C. Heath; 2. Sarah Putnam/©D.C. Heath; 3. John Owens/©D.C. Heath; 4. Nita Winter/The Image Works; 5,6 Sarah Putnam/©D.C. Heath; Bottom row 1. John Owens/©D.C. Heath; 2. Sarah Putnam/©D.C. Heath; 3. John Owens/©D.C. Heath; 4 *t* Julie Bidwell/©D.C. Heath, *b* Jim Whitmer/Stock Boston; 5 *t* Richard Haynes/©D.C. Heath, *b* Sarah Putnam/©D.C. Heath.
Cover Design: Robin Herr

Copyright © 1995 by D.C. Heath and Company

Acknowledgments for copyrighted material are on page 125 and constitute an extension of this page.

All rights reserved. No part of this publication may be reproduced or transmitted in any form by any means, electronic or mechanical, including photocopy, recording, or any information storage or retrieval system, without permission in writing from the publisher.

Published simultaneously in Canada

Printed in the United States of America

International Standard Book Number: 0-669-32109-5 (soft cover); 0-669-38178-0 (hard cover)
2 3 4 5 6 7 8 9 10-RRD-99 98 97 96 95 94

Middle Level Authors

Donna Alvermann, University of Georgia
Alice Haskins, Howard County Public Schools, Maryland
J. Howard Johnston, University of South Florida
John Lounsbury, Georgia College
Sandra Schurr, University of South Florida
Julia Thomason, Appalachian State University
Max Thompson, Appalachian State University
Carl Zon, California Assessment Collaborative

Literature and Language Arts Authors

Linda Miller Cleary, University of Minnesota
Kenneth Donelson, Arizona State University
Donald Gallo, Central Connecticut State University
Alleen Pace Nilsen, Arizona State University
Robert Pavlik, Cardinal Stritch College, Milwaukee
Jewell Parker Rhodes, Arizona State University
Alberto Alvaro Ríos, Arizona State University
Lyndon Searfoss, Arizona State University

Teacher Consultants

Suzanne Aubin, Patapsco Middle School, Ellicott City, Maryland
Judy Baxter, Newport News Public Schools, Newport News, Virginia
Saundra Bryn, Director of Research and Development, El Mirage, Arizona
Lorraine Gerhart, Elmbrook Middle School, Elm Grove, Wisconsin
Kathy Tuchman Glass, Burlingame Intermediate School, Burlingame, California
Lucretia Pannozzo, John Jay Middle School, Katonah, New York
Carol Schultz, Jerling Junior High, Orland Park, Illinois
Jeanne Siebenman, Grand Canyon University, Phoenix, Arizona
Gail Thompson, Garey High School, Pomona, California
Rufus Thompson, Grace Yokley School, Ontario, California
Tom Tufts, Conniston Middle School, West Palm Beach, Florida
Edna Turner, Harpers Choice Middle School, Columbia, Maryland
C. Anne Webb, Buerkle Junior High School, St. Louis, Missouri
Geri Yaccino, Thompson Junior High School, St. Charles, Illinois

CONTENTS

THE LITERATURE

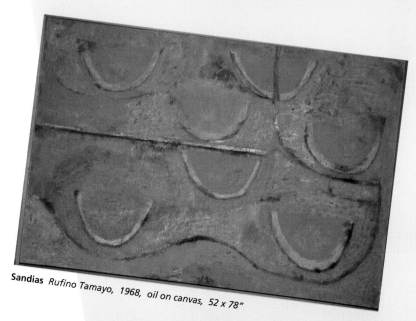

Sandias *Rufino Tamayo, 1968, oil on canvas, 52 x 78"*

ASKING BIG QUESTIONS ABOUT THE LITERATURE

PROJECTS

1 WRITING WORKSHOP
WEAR A CRITIC'S HAT 106-111

Choose a book, movie, or piece of literature to evaluate. Then write a review for other students, giving the work a thumbs up or a thumbs down.

2 COOPERATIVE LEARNING
WELCOME TO MIDDLE SCHOOL! 112-113

Do you remember starting middle school? What was your biggest challenge? Create an orientation packet for sixth graders, drawing upon your own prior experiences and past concerns.

3 HELPING YOUR COMMUNITY
VOICES FROM THE PAST 114-115

Interview an adult about changes, choices, and challenges that he or she has experienced in life. Record the interview as part of a class oral history project.

WHAT if...

You and a classmate have been best friends since third grade. But lately you don't talk to each other much. And when you do speak, your friend is cold and abrupt. Then, one day during lunch, you discover that your friend isn't sitting at your customary table. When you scan the lunchroom, you can't believe your eyes. Your friend has abandoned you for another group at school.

Suddenly, your whole world has changed, and you don't know what to do. But help is on the way. In this activity, you'll work with a partner or a group to learn how to make choices when faced with challenges.

START ▶

1 Pick a dilemma.

With your partner or group, pick a dilemma on which to practice. Choose the dilemma in the blue panel above, pick one from the game cards on this page, or use a dilemma from your own life.

When a good friend tells you a secret, you promise not to tell anyone else. Then, by accident, you let the secret slip. You want to regain your friend's trust, but you don't know how.

The kids in your crowd want to make some prank phone calls. "Come on," they tell you, "we'll have fun, and no one will get hurt." When you say you'd rather not, they call you a baby and walk away. You want to stick by your principles, but you also want to keep your friends.

One night, you and your friends sneak into the yard of the neighborhood grouch and cut down a small rose bush. The next day, you're astonished to see him standing in his yard trembling and crying. Suddenly he doesn't appear mean at all but just a lonely old man in need of friendship.

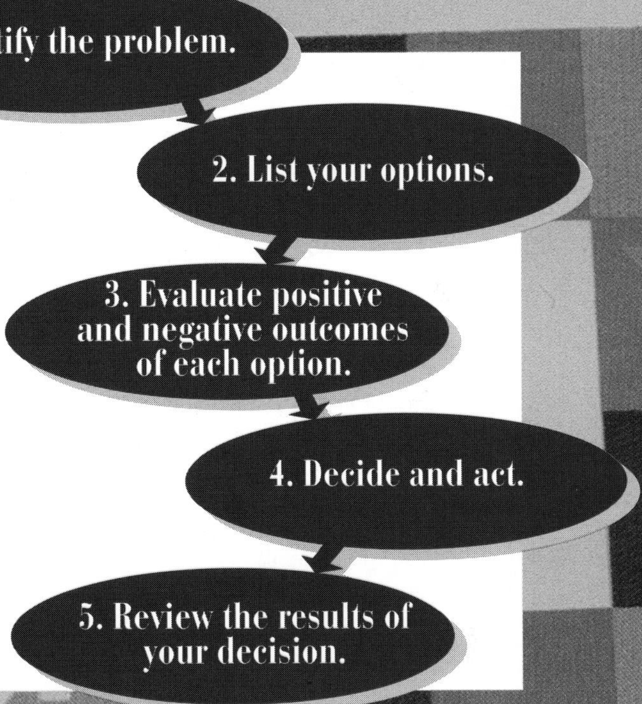

2 Learn how to make a decision.

Some people don't make decisions until they're forced to, and then they decide based on their emotions at the time. Decisions made this way are not the best. A better way is to make decisions based on careful thought and analysis.

Look at the diagram on the right. It lists the five steps of the decision-making process. It will help you as you try to solve your dilemma.

> 1. Identify the problem.

> 2. List your options.

> 3. Evaluate positive and negative outcomes of each option.

> 4. Decide and act.

> 5. Review the results of your decision.

3 Solve your dilemma.

Use the five steps in the diagram above to help you reach a solution to the dilemma you selected.

- Choose one person in your group to record ideas and thoughts about each step.
- Work with your group to form a **consensus** about how you would deal with the dilemma. In a consensus, each of you agrees about a course of action. Have the recorder write down your decision.

4 Compare results.

- Choose a spokesperson for your group to share your dilemma and your decision with the rest of the class.
- Compare your decision with groups who chose the same dilemma. How are the decisions similar? Different? What was most difficult about making a decision? What part of the process surprised you?

Asking Big Questions About the Theme

What kinds of changes do people experience?

In your journal, draw two pictures. In the first picture, show the way you looked a year ago. Did you wear braces? Enjoy basketball? Have long hair? Were you short or tall, happy or moody, carefree or worried? In the second picture, show yourself today. In a paragraph, describe how you have changed. Include examples not shown in your drawings, such as changes within your family or among your friends.

What challenges result from these changes?

In your journal, draw a cause-and-effect diagram like the one shown. In the box labeled *Change*, write one change you have experienced during the past year. In each of the boxes labeled *Challenge*, write a challenge you have faced as a result of this change. Finally, beneath your diagram, write several sentences about the challenge that seems most important to you.

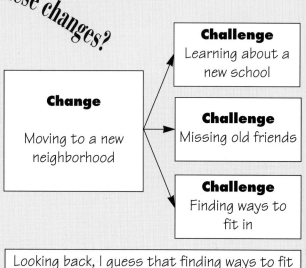

Change

Moving to a new neighborhood

Challenge
Learning about a new school

Challenge
Missing old friends

Challenge
Finding ways to fit in

Looking back, I guess that finding ways to fit in was the most difficult for me...

What choices do people make when faced with challenges?

Imagine that you have moved to a new neighborhood. What would you do to meet each of the following challenges?

- Learn about your new school
- Keep in touch with old friends
- Find ways to fit in

In your journal, write about the choices you might make. Then discuss your choices with a partner or a group.

What qualities help people face change successfully?

What qualities help you deal with changes? In your journal, create a cluster or web like the one that has been started. Include traits or qualities that help you confront change. (It may help to think of specific changes, such as moving to a new community.) Then work with classmates to make a large web or cluster of qualities that you can post in the classroom.

NOW

Think!

What is the most important change you have faced in life? How have you handled this change? As you read "Changes and Choices," think about this change. Compare your experiences in facing change with the experiences of the characters in the selections. What do the characters say to you about dealing with changes successfully?

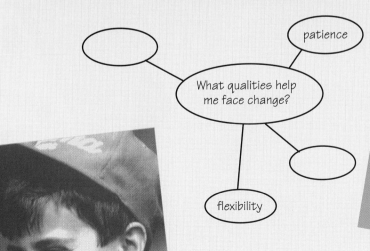

patience

What qualities help me face change?

flexibility

GROWING UP

GARY SOTO

Now that Maria was a tenth-grader, she felt she was too grown-up to have to go on family vacations. Last year, the family had driven three hundred miles to see their uncle in West Covina. There was nothing to do. The days were hot, with a yellow sky thick with smog they could feel on their fingertips. They played cards and watched game shows on television. After the first four days of doing nothing while the grown-ups sat around talking, the kids finally got to go to Disneyland.

Disneyland stood tall with castles and bright flags. The Matterhorn[1] had wild dips and curves that took your breath away if you closed your eyes and screamed. The Pirates of the Caribbean didn't scare anyone but was fun anyway, and so were the teacups and It's a Small World. The parents spoiled the kids, giving each of them five dollars to spend on trinkets. Maria's younger sister, Irma, bought a Pinocchio coloring book and a candy bracelet. Her brothers, Rudy and John, spent their money on candy that made their teeth blue.

1. **Matterhorn** [matʹ ər hôrn]: a ride at Disneyland in California patterned on a mountain peak in the Alps between Switzerland and Italy.

Maria saved her money. She knew everything was over-priced, like the Mickey Mouse balloons you could get for a fraction of the price in Fresno. Of course, the balloon at Hanoian's supermarket didn't have a Mickey Mouse face, but it would bounce and float and eventually pop like any other balloon.

Maria folded her five dollars, tucked it in her red purse, and went on rides until she got sick. After that, she sat on a bench, jealously watching other teenage girls who seemed much better dressed than she was. She felt stricken by poverty. All the screaming kids in nice clothes probably came from homes with swimming pools in their backyards, she thought. Yes, her father was a foreman at a paper mill, and yes, she had a Dough-boy swimming pool in her backyard, but *still*, things were not the same. She had felt poor, and her sun dress, which seemed snappy in Fresno, was out of style at Disneyland, where every other kid was wearing Esprit shirts and Guess jeans.

This year Maria's family planned to visit an uncle in San Jose. Her father promised to take them to Great America,[2] but she knew that the grown-ups would sit around talking for days before they remembered the kids and finally got up and did something. They would have to wait until the last day before they could go to Great America. It wasn't worth the boredom.

"Dad, I'm not going this year," Maria said to her father. He sat at the table with the newspaper in front of him.

"What do you mean?" he asked, slowly looking up. He thought a moment and said, "When I was a kid we didn't have the money for vacations. I would have been happy to go with my father."

"I know, I know. You've said that a hundred times," she snapped.

"What did you say?" he asked, pushing his newspaper aside.

Everything went quiet. Maria could hear the hum of the refrigerator and her brothers out in the front yard arguing over a popsicle

2. **Great America:** an amusement park in California.

stick, and her mother in the backyard watering the strip of grass that ran along the patio.

Her father's eyes locked on her with a dark stare. Maria had seen that stare before. She pleaded in a soft daughterly voice, "We never do anything. It's boring. Don't you understand?"

"No, I don't understand. I work all year, and if I want to go on a vacation, then I go. And my family goes too." He took a swallow of ice water, and glared.

"You have it so easy," he continued. "In Chihuahua,[3] my town, we worked hard. You worked, even *los chavalos!*[4] And you showed respect to your parents, something you haven't learned."

Here it comes, Maria thought, stories about his childhood in Mexico. She wanted to stuff her ears with wads of newspaper to keep from hearing him. She could recite his stories word-for-word. She couldn't wait until she was in college and away from them.

"Do you know my father worked in the mines? That he nearly lost his life? And today his lungs are bad." He pounded his chest with hard, dirt-creased knuckles.

Maria pushed back her hair and looked out the window at her brothers running around in the front yard. She couldn't stand it anymore. She got up and walked away, and when he yelled for her to come back, she ignored him. She locked herself in her bedroom and tried to read *Seventeen*, though she could hear her father complaining to her mother, who had come in when she had heard the yelling.

"*Habla con tu mocosa,*"[5] she heard him say.

She heard the refrigerator door open. He was probably getting a beer, a "cold one," as he would say. She flipped through the pages of her magazine and stopped at a Levi's ad of a girl about her age walking between two

---

3. **Chihuahua** [chi wä′ wä]: a state in northern Mexico; its capital has the same name.
4. *los chavalos* [lōs chä vä′ lōs]: Spanish for "young boys."
5. *Habla con tu mocosa* [ä′ blä con tü mō kō′ sä]: Spanish for "Talk to your brat."

happy-looking guys on a beach. She wished she were that girl, that she had another life. She turned the page and thought, I bet you he gets drunk and drives crazy tomorrow.

Maria's mother was putting away a pitcher of Kool-Aid the boys had left out. She looked at her husband, who was fumbling with a wadded-up napkin. His eyes were dark, and his thoughts were on Mexico, where a father was respected and his word, right or wrong, was final. "Rafael, she's growing up; she's a teenager. She talks like that, but she still loves you."

"Sure, and that's how she shows her love, by talking back to her father." He rubbed the back of his neck and turned his head trying to make the stiffness go away. He knew it was true, but he was the man of the house and no daughter of his was going to tell him what to do.

Instead, it was his wife, Eva, who told him what to do. "Let the girl stay. She's big now. She don't want to go on rides no more. She can stay with her *nina*."[6]

The father drank his beer and argued, but eventually agreed to let his daughter stay.

The family rose just after six the next day and was ready to go by seven-thirty. Maria stayed in her room. She wanted to apologize to her father but couldn't. She knew that if she said, "Dad, I'm sorry," she would break into tears. Her father wanted to come into her room and say, "We'll do something really special this vacation. Come with us, honey." But it was hard for him to show his emotions around his children, especially when he tried to make up to them.

6. *nina* [nē′ nä]: Spanish for "godmother."

The mother kissed Maria. "Maria, I want you to clean the house and then walk over to your *nina*'s. I want no monkey business while we're gone, do you hear me?"

"*Sí*, Mama."

"Here's the key. You water the plants inside and turn on the sprinkler every couple of days." She handed Maria the key and hugged her. "You be good. Now, come say goodbye to your father."

Reluctantly, she walked out in her robe to the front yard and, looking down at the ground, said goodbye to her father. The father looked down and said goodbye to the garden hose at his feet.

After they left, Maria lounged in her pajamas listening to the radio and thumbing through magazines. Then she got up, fixed herself a bowl of Cocoa Puffs, and watched "American Bandstand."[7] Her dream was to dance on the show, to look at the camera, smile, and let everyone in Fresno see that she could have a good time, too.

But an ill feeling stirred inside her. She felt awful about arguing with her father. She felt bad for her mother and two brothers, who would have to spend the next three hours in the car with him. Maybe he would do something crazy, like crash the car on purpose to get back at her, or fall asleep and run the car into an irrigation ditch. And it would be her fault.

7. **American Bandstand:** TV program that featured the studio audience dancing to popular music.

She turned the radio to a news station. She listened for half an hour, but most of the news was about warships in the Persian Gulf and a tornado in Texas. There was no mention of her family.

Maria began to calm down because, after all, her father was really nice beneath his gruffness. She dressed slowly, made some swishes with the broom in the kitchen, and let the hose run in a flower bed while she painted her toenails with her mother's polish. Afterward, she called her friend Becky to tell her that her parents had let her stay home, that she was free—for five days at least.

"Great," Becky said. "I wish my mom and dad would go away and let me stay by myself."

"No, I have to stay with my godmother." She made a mental note to give her *nina* a call. "Becky, let's go to the mall and check out the boys."

"All right."

"I'll be over pretty soon."

Maria called her *nina*, who said it was OK for her to go shopping, but to be at her house for dinnertime by six. After hanging up, Maria took off her jeans and T-shirt, and changed into a dress. She went through her mother's closet to borrow a pair of shoes and drenched her wrists in Charlie perfume. She put on coral-pink lipstick and a smudge of blue eyeshadow. She felt beautiful, although a little self-conscious. She took off some of the lipstick and ran water over her wrists to dilute the fragrance.

While she walked the four blocks to Becky's house, she beamed happiness until she passed a man who was on his knees pulling weeds from his flower bed. At his side, a radio was reporting a traffic accident. A big rig had overturned after hitting a car near Salinas, twenty miles from San Jose.

A wave of fear ran through her. Maybe it was *them*. Her smile disappeared, and her shoulders slouched. No, it couldn't be, she thought. Salinas is not that close to San Jose. Then again, maybe her father wanted to travel through Salinas because it was a pretty valley with wide plains and oak trees, and horses and cows that stared as you passed them in your speeding car. But maybe it did happen; maybe they had gotten in an awful wreck.

By the time she got to Becky's house, she was riddled with guilt, since it was she who would have disturbed her father and made him crash.

"Hi," she said to Becky, trying to look cheerful.

"You look terrific, Maria," Becky said. "Mom, look at Maria. Come inside for a bit."

Maria blushed when Becky's mother said she looked gorgeous. She didn't know what to do except stare at the carpet and say, "Thank you, Mrs. Ledesma."

Becky's mother gave them a ride to the mall, but they'd have to take a bus back. The girls first went to Macy's, where they hunted for a sweater, something flashy but not too flashy. Then they left to have a Coke and sit by the fountain under an artificial tree. They watched people walk by, especially the boys, who, they agreed, were dumb but cute nevertheless.

They went to The Gap, where they tried on some skirts, and ventured into The Limited, where they walked up and down the aisles breathing in the rich smells of 100-percent wool and silk. They were about to leave, when Maria heard once again on someone's portable radio that a family had been killed in an auto accident near Salinas. Maria stopped smiling for a moment as she pictured her family's overturned Malibu station wagon.

Becky sensed that something was wrong and asked, "How come you're so quiet?"

Maria forced a smile. "Oh, nothing, I was just thinking."

" 'bout what?"

Maria thought quickly. "Oh, I think I left the water on at home." This could have been true. Maria remembered pulling the hose from the flower bed, but couldn't remember if she had turned the water off.

Afterward they rode the bus home with nothing to show for their three hours of shopping except a small bag of See's candies. But it had been a good day. Two boys had followed them, joking and flirting, and they had flirted back. The girls gave them made-up telephone numbers, then turned away and laughed into their hands.

"They're fools," Becky said, "but cute."

Maria left Becky when they got off the bus, and started off to her *nina*'s house. Then she remembered that the garden hose might still be running at home. She hurried home, clip-clopping clumsily in her mother's shoes.

The garden hose was rolled neatly against the trellis. Maria decided to check the mail and went inside. When she pushed open the door, the living room gave off a quietness she had never heard before. Usually the TV was on, her younger brothers and sister were playing, and her mother could be heard in the kitchen. When the telephone rang, Maria jumped. She kicked off her shoes, ran to the phone, and picked up the receiver only to hear a distant clicking sound.

"Hello, hello?" Maria's heart began to thump. Her mind went wild with possibilities. An accident, she thought, they're in an accident, and it's all my fault. "Who is it? Dad? Mom?"

She hung up and looked around the room. The clock on the television set glowed 5:15. She gathered the mail, changed into jeans, and left for her *nina*'s house with a shopping bag containing her nightie and a toothbrush.

Her *nina* was happy to see her. She took Maria's head in her hands and gave it a loud kiss.

"Dinner is almost ready," she said, gently pulling her inside.

"Oh, good. Becky and I only had popcorn for lunch."

They had a quiet evening together. After dinner, they sat on the porch watching the stars. Maria wanted to ask her *nina* if she had heard from her parents. She wanted to know if the police had called to report that they had gotten into an accident. But she just sat on the porch swing, letting anxiety eat a hole in her soul.

The family was gone for four days. Maria prayed for them, prayed that she would not wake up to a phone call saying that their car had been found in a ditch. She made a list of the ways she could be nicer to them: doing the dishes without being asked, watering the lawn, hugging her father after work, and playing with her youngest brother, even if it bored her to tears.

At night Maria worried herself sick listening to the radio for news of an accident. She thought of her uncle Shorty and how he fell asleep and crashed his car in the small town of Mendota. He lived confined to a motorized wheelchair and was scarred with burns on the left side of his face.

"Oh, please, don't let anything like that happen to them," she prayed.

In the morning she could barely look at the newspaper. She feared that if she unfolded it, the front page would feature a story about a family from Fresno who had flown off the roller coaster at Great America. Or that a shark had attacked them as they bobbed happily among the white-tipped waves. Something awful is going to happen, she said to herself as she poured Rice Krispies into a bowl.

But nothing happened. Her family returned home, dark from lying on the beach and full of great stories about the Santa Cruz boardwalk and Great America and an Egyptian museum. They had done more this year than in all their previous vacations.

"Oh, we had fun," her mother said, pounding sand from her shoes before entering the house.

Her father gave her a tight hug as her brothers ran by, dark from hours of swimming.

Maria stared at the floor, miffed. How dare they have so much fun? While she worried herself sick about them, they had splashed in the waves, stayed at Great America until nightfall, and eaten at all kinds of restaurants. They even went shopping for fall school clothes.

Feeling resentful as Johnny described a ride that dropped straight down and threw your stomach into your mouth, Maria turned away and went off to her bedroom, where she kicked off her shoes and thumbed through an old *Seventeen*. Her family was alive and as obnoxious as ever. She took back all her promises. From now on she would keep to herself and ignore them. When they asked, "Maria, would you help me," she would pretend not to hear and walk away.

"They're heartless," she muttered. "Here I am worrying about them, and there they are having fun." She thought of the rides they had gone on, the hours of body surfing, the handsome boys she didn't get to see, the restaurants, and the museum. Her eyes filled with tears. For the first time in years, she hugged a doll, the one her grand-mother Lupe had stitched together from rags and old clothes.

"Something's wrong with me," she cried softly. She turned on her radio and heard about a single-engined plane that had crashed in Cupertino, a city not far from San Jose. She thought of the plane and the people inside, how the pilot's family would suffer.

She hugged her doll. Something was happening to her, and it might be that she was growing up. When the news ended, and a song started playing, she got up and washed her face without looking in the mirror.

That night the family went out for Chinese food. Although her brothers fooled around, cracked jokes, and spilled a soda, she was happy. She ate a lot, and when her fortune cookie said, "You are mature and sensible," she had to agree. And her father and mother did too. The family drove home singing the words to "La Bamba" along with the car radio.

GARY SOTO

Gary Soto was born in Fresno, California, in 1952 and grew up in the San Joaquin Valley, where he was a migrant farm worker. When he entered college he planned to study geography, but soon found that he was more interested in literature.

Soto is best known as a poet. His first collection of poetry, *The Elements of San Joaquin*, won the United States Award of the International Poetry Forum. He continues to write poetry and is thought of as one of the country's most important poets. Soto teaches English and Chicano Studies at the University of California, in Berkeley.

Soto did not publish prose until 1985, but since then he has become well known for his autobiographical essays and sketches. Most of these focus on his childhood and his teen years growing up in a Mexican American family. "Growing Up" is from a collection of autobiographical stories titled *Baseball in April and Other Stories*. Other such collections are *A Summer Life* and *Pacific Crossing*.

Curtains Roy Lichtenstein, 1962, oil and magna on canvas, 68$\frac{3}{4}$" x 58$\frac{1}{2}$", The St. Louis Art Museum

As It Is with Strangers

SUSAN BETH PFEFFER

It wasn't until right before I went to bed on Thursday that Mom bothered to tell me the son she'd given up for adoption twenty years earlier was coming over for supper the next day.

"What son?" I asked.

"I'm sure I've told you about him," Mom said. "You must have forgotten."

I figured I probably had. I'm always forgetting little things like my homework assignments and being elected President of the United States. Having an older brother must have just slipped my mind. "How'd you two find each other?" I asked. Presumably Mom had never told me that.

"I registered with an agency," she said. "Put my name and address in a book, so if he ever wanted to find me, he could. I guess he did. Don't be late for supper tomorrow."

"I won't be," I promised. This was one reunion I had no intention of missing.

School the next day really dragged on. School never goes fast on Fridays, but when your mind is on some newly acquired half brother, it's real hard to care about Julius Caesar. I didn't tell anybody, though. It seemed to me it was Mom's story, not mine, and besides, my friends all think she's crazy anyway. Probably from things I've said over the years.

I went straight home from school, and was surprised, first to find the place spotless, and then to see Mom in the kitchen cooking away.

"I took a sick day," she informed me. "So I could prepare better."

"Everything looks great," I told her. It was true. I hadn't seen the place look so good since Great-Aunt Trudy came with the goat, but that's another story. "You look very pretty too."

"I got my nails done," Mom said, showing them off for me. They were coral colored. "And my hair."

I nodded. Mom had taught me that nothing was unbearable if your hair looked nice.

"Is that what you're planning to wear tonight?" she asked.

"I thought I'd shower and change into my dress," I said. I own a grand total of one dress, but this seemed to be the right kind of occasion for it.

Mom gave me a smile like I'd just been canonized. "Thank you," she said. "Tonight's kind of important for me."

I nodded. I wasn't sure just what to say anymore. Mom and I have been alone for eight years, and you'd figure by now I'd know how to handle her under any circumstances, but this one had me stumped. "What's for supper?" I finally asked.

"Southern fried chicken," Mom said. "At first I thought I'd make a roast, but then what if he doesn't like his meat rare? And turkey seemed too Thanksgivingish, if you know what I mean. Everybody likes fried chicken. And I made mashed potatoes and biscuits and a spinach salad."

"Spinach salad?" I asked. I could picture Mom pouring the spinach out of a can and dousing it with Wishbone.

"From scratch," Mom informed me. "Everything's from scratch.

And I baked an apple pie too. The ice cream is store bought, but I got one of those expensive brands. What do you think?"

I thought that there obviously was something to that Prodigal Son[1] story, since Mom never made anything more elaborate for me than scrambled eggs. "It smells great," I said. It did, too, the way you picture a house in a commercial smelling, all homey and warm. "I'm sure everything will go fine."

"I want it to," Mom said, as though I'd suggested that maybe she didn't.

There were a few things I knew I'd better clear up before Big Brother showed up. "What's his name?" I asked, for starters.

"Jack," Mom said. "That's not what I would have named him. I would have named him Ronald."

"You would have?" I asked. I personally am named Tiffany, and Ronald would not have been my first guess.

"That was my boyfriend's name," Mom said. "Ronny."

"Your boyfriend," I said. "You mean his father?"

Mom nodded. "You think of them as boyfriends, not fathers, when you're sixteen," she said.

Well that answered question number two. It had seemed unlikely to me that my father was responsible, but who knew? I wasn't there. Maybe he and Mom had decided they wanted a girl, and chucked out any boys that came along first.

Speaking of which. "There aren't any other brothers I've forgotten about?" I asked. "Is this going to be the first of many such dinners?"

"Jack's the only one," Mom replied. "I wanted to keep him, but Ronny wasn't about to get married, and Dad said if I gave him up for adoption then I could still go to college. I did the right thing, for him and for me. And I would have gone to college if I hadn't met your father. I don't know. Maybe because I gave up the baby, I was too eager to get married. I never really thought about it."

"Did Dad know?" I asked.

1. **Prodigal Son** [prod′ ə gəl]: story in the New Testament of the Bible concerning a reckless son who returns home and asks and receives forgiveness from his father.

Turkey Roy Lichtenstein, 1961, oil on canvas, 26" x 30", ©Roy Lichtenstein, photo by Robert McKeever

"I told him," Mom said. "He said it didn't matter to him. And it didn't. Whatever else was wrong in our marriage, he never threw the baby in my face."

I found myself picturing a baby being thrown in Mom's face, and decided I should take my shower fast. So I sniffed the kitchen appreciatively and scurried out. In the shower I tried to imagine what this Jack would look like, but he kept resembling Dad's high-school graduation picture, which made no sense biologically at all. So I stopped imagining.

When I went to my bedroom to change, though, I was really shocked. Mom had extended her cleaning ways to include my room. All my carefully laid out messes were gone. It would probably take me months to reassemble things. I considered screaming at Mom

Cherry Pie Roy Lichtenstein, 1962, oil on canvas, 20" x 24", Collection of Sydney and Frances Lewis

about the sanctity of one's bedroom, but I decided against it. Mom obviously wanted this guy to think she and I were the perfect American family, and if that meant even my room had to be clean, then nothing was going to stop her. I could live with it, at least for the evening.

Mom and I set the table three times before the doorbell finally rang. When it did, neither one of us knew who should answer it, but Mom finally opened the door. "Hello," this guy said. "I'm Jack."

"I'm Linda," Mom replied. "Come on in. It's nice to . . . well, it's good seeing you."

"Good to see you too," Jack said. He didn't look anything like my father.

"This is Tiffany," Mom said. "She, uh . . ."

"Her daughter," I said. "Your sister." I mean, those words were going to be used at some point during the evening. We might as well get them out of the way fast. Then when we got around to the big tricky words like *mother* and *son*, at least some groundwork would have been laid.

"It's nice to meet you," Jack said, and he gave me his hand to shake, so I shook it. They say you can tell a lot about a man from his handshake, but not when he's your long-lost brother. "I hope my coming like this isn't any kind of a brother. I mean bother."

"Not at all," Mom said. "I'm going to check on dinner. Tiffany, why don't you show Jack the living room? I'll join you in a moment."

"This is the living room," I said, which was pretty easy to show Jack, since we were already standing in it. "Want to sit down?"

"Yeah, sure," Jack said. "Have you lived here long?"

"Since the divorce," I said. "Eight years ago."

"That long," Jack said. "Where's your father?"

"He lives in Oak Ridge," I said. "That's a couple of hundred miles from here. I see him sometimes."

"Is he . . ." Jack began. "I mean, I don't suppose you'd know . . ."

"Is he your father too?" I said. "No. I kind of asked. Your father's name is Ronny. My father's name is Mike. I don't know much else about your father except he didn't want to marry Mom. They were both teenagers, I guess. Do you want to meet him too?"

"Sometime," Jack said. "Not tonight."

I could sure understand that one. "I've always wanted to have a big brother," I told him. "I always had crushes on my friends' big brothers. Did you want that—to have a kid sister, I mean?"

"I have one," Jack said. "No, I guess now I have two. I have a sister back home. Her name is Leigh Ann. She's adopted too. She's Korean."

"Oh," I said. "That's nice. I guess there isn't much of a family resemblance, then."

"Not much," Jack said, but he smiled. "She's twelve. How old are you?"

"Fifteen," I said. "Do you go to college?"

Jack nodded. "I'm a sophomore at Bucknell," he said. "Do you think you'll go to college?"

"I'd like to," I said. "I don't know if we'll have the money, though."

"It's rough," Jack said. "College costs a lot these days. My father's always griping about it. He owns a car dealership. New and used. I work there summers. My mom's a housewife."

I wanted to tell him how hard Mom had worked on supper, how messy the apartment usually was, how I never wore a dress, and Mom's nails were always a deep sinful scarlet. I wanted to tell him that maybe someday I'd be jealous that he'd been given away to a family that could afford to send him to college, but that it was too soon for me to feel much of anything about him. There was a lot I wanted to say, but I didn't say any of it.

"What's she like?" Jack asked me, and he gestured toward the kitchen, as though I might not otherwise know who he was talking about.

"Mom?" I said. "She's terrible. She drinks and she gambles and she beats me black and blue if I even think something wrong."

Jack looked horrified. I realized he had definitely not inherited Mom's sense of humor.

"I'm only kidding," I said. "I haven't even been spanked since I was five. She's fine. She's a good mother. It must have really hurt her to give you away like that."

"Have you known long?" Jack asked. "About me?"

"Not until recently," I said. It didn't seem right to tell him I'd learned less than twenty-four hours before. "I guess Mom was waiting until I was old enough to understand."

"I always knew I was adopted," Jack said. "And for years I've wanted to meet my biological parents. To see what they looked like. I love Mom and Dad, you understand. But I felt this need."

"I can imagine," I said, and I could too. I was starting to develop a real need to see what Jack's parents looked like, and we weren't even related.

"Tiffany, could you come in here for a minute?" Mom called from the kitchen.

"Coming, Mom," I said, and left the living room fast. It takes a lot out of you making small talk with a brother.

"What do you think?" Mom whispered as soon as she saw me. "Does he look like me?"

"He has your eyes," I said. "And I think he has your old hair color."

"I know," Mom said, patting her bottle red hair. "I almost asked them to dye me back to my original shade, but I wasn't sure I could remember it anymore. Do you like him? Does he seem nice?"

"Very nice," I said. "Very good manners."

"He sure didn't inherit those from Ronny," Mom declared. "Come on, let's start taking the food out."

So we did. We carried out platters of chicken and mashed potatoes and biscuits and salad. Jack came to the table as soon as he saw what we were doing.

"Oh, no," he said. "I mean, I'm sorry. I should have told you. I'm a vegetarian."

"You are?" Mom said. She looked as shocked as if he'd told her he was a vampire. Meat is very important to Mom. "You're not sick or anything, are you?"

"No, it's for moral reasons," Jack said. "It drives my mom, my mother, her name's Cathy, it drives Cathy crazy."

"Your mom," my mom said. "It would drive me crazy, too, if Tiffany stopped eating meat just for moral reasons."

"Don't worry about it," I told her. "I'll never be that moral."

"There's plenty for me to eat," Jack said. "Potatoes and biscuits and salad."

"The salad has bacon in it," Mom said. "I crumbled bacon in it."

"We can wash the bacon off, can't we Jack?" I said. "You'll eat it if we wash the bacon off, won't you?"

I thought he hesitated for a moment, but then he said, "Of course I can," and for the first time since we'd met, I kind of liked him. I took the salad into the kitchen and washed it all. The salad dressing went the way of the bacon, but we weren't about to complain. At least there'd be something green on Jack's plate. All his other food was gray-white.

Mom hardly ate her chicken, which I figured was out of deference to the vegetarian, but I had two and a half pieces, figuring it might be years before Mom made it again. Jack ate more potatoes than I'd ever seen another human being eat. No gravy, but lots of potatoes. We talked polite stuff during dinner, what he was studying in college, where Mom worked, the adjustments Leigh Ann had had to make. The real things could only be discussed one on one, so after the pie and ice cream, I excused myself and went to Mom's room to watch TV. Only I couldn't make my eyes focus, so I crossed the hall to my room, and recreated my messes. Once I had everything in proper order, though, I put things back the way Mom had had them. I could hear them talking while I moved piles around, and then I turned on my radio, so I couldn't even hear the occasional stray word, like *father* and *high school* and *lawyer*. That was a trick I'd learned years ago, when Mom and Dad were in their fighting stage. The radio played a lot of old songs that night. It made me feel like I was seven all over again.

After a while Mom knocked on my door and said Jack was leaving, so I went to the living room and shook hands with him again. I still couldn't tell anything about his personality from his handshake, but he did have good manners, and he gave me a little pecking kiss on my cheek, which I thought was sweet of him. Mom kept the door open, and watched as he walked the length of the corridor to the stairs. She didn't close the door until he'd gotten into a car, his I assumed. Maybe it was a loaner from his father.

"You give away a baby," Mom said, "and twenty years later he turns up on your doorstep a vegetarian."

"He turns up a turnip," I said.

But Mom wasn't in the mood for those kinds of jokes. "Don't you ever make that mistake," she said.

"What mistake?" I asked, afraid she meant making jokes. If I couldn't make jokes with Mom, I wouldn't know how to talk with her.

"Don't you ever give up something so important to you that it breathes when you do," Mom said. "It doesn't have to be a kid. It can be a dream, an ambition, or a marriage, or a house. It can be anything

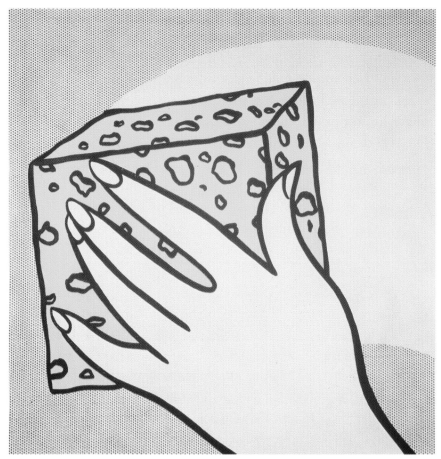

Sponge II Roy Lichtenstein, 1962, oil on canvas, 36"x 36", ©Roy Lichtenstein

you care about as deeply as you care about your own life. Don't ever just give it away, because you'll spend the rest of your life wondering about it, or pretending you don't wonder, which is the same thing, and you'll wake up one morning and realize it truly is gone and a big part of you is gone with it. Do you hear me, Tiffany?"

"I hear you," I said. I'd never seen Mom so intense, and I didn't like being around her. "I'm kind of tired now, Mom. Would you mind if I went to bed early?"

"I'll clean up tomorrow," Mom said. "You can go to bed."

So I did. I left her sitting in the living room and went to my bedroom and closed my door. But this time I didn't turn the radio on, and later, when I'd been lying on my bed for hours, not able to sleep, I could hear her in her room crying. I'd heard her cry in her room a hundred times before, and a hundred times before I'd gotten up and comforted her, and I knew she'd cry a hundred times again, and I'd comfort her then, too, but that night I just stayed in my room, on my bed, staring at the ceiling and listening to her cry. I think I did the right thing, not going in there. That's how it is with strangers. You can never really comfort them.

S U S A N   B E T H   P F E F F E R

Susan Beth Pfeffer, who was born in New York City in 1948, has written a number of young-adult novels about important teenage issues concerning home, school, and work. "My interests range from baseball to medieval art," she says, "with stops at movie history, the lives of innumerable writers, and local theater. I've been writing since age six when I completed my first novel, *Dookie the Cookie*." That first novel is still unpublished, but one that is available is called *Better Than All Right*.

THE TORN INVITATION

NORMAN KATKOV

At fifteen, in the spring of his sophomore year at Hamilton High School, Harry Wojick was as big as a college senior, a long, thin, big-boned left-hander, who could anchor a leg in first base and stretch halfway to right field for a bad throw from his shortstop.

Now, in the waning daylight, he turned into Glover Street toward his home, his arms swinging as he moved onto the unpaved road. For a few feet he ran easily, bringing his knees up high, until, without warning, he stopped short and bent low to field the imaginary ball cleanly, beating the runner by a mile. He straightened up, grinning in the half darkness, blushing a little from the applause at the brilliant play he had made.

Harry Wojick came off the street onto the opposite sidewalk. He passed the four-family flat in the middle of the block. He passed the empty lot and beyond it the condemned building with all the windows long since broken, and then he turned into the cement walk which ran the length of his house.

Mother and Child Elizabeth Catlett, 1972, pecan wood, courtesy of the Museum of African-American Art

The windows were raised in the kitchen and he smelled the roast. He smelled the asparagus for the roast and the fried potatoes with onions that nobody made like Ma, and he was suddenly terribly hungry after the three hours of baseball practice.

When he came into the kitchen, Theresa Wojick turned from the stove, smiling at her son, rubbing her hands on her apron as she walked to meet him. She held him at the elbows, examining him carefully, her face warm and her eyes gentle, welcoming him as though he had returned from a long and perilous journey. She was a tall woman with large, capable hands and black, unkempt hair shot through with gray. She held Harry and she said, "Hello, my little son. Will you eat supper?" joking with him as always.

He put his cheek to hers, noticing again the redness of her chapped hands. She could try to do something about it, he said to himself, as she released him, remembering the mothers of his teammates who lived above the flats on Livingston Drive and Harding Boulevard and scattered through Maple Heights. They were mothers with manicures and they were thin—and their hair was always set just right.

Harry went to the sink to wash and, turning, saw the table set for three. He thought for an instant that his father was home, that Peter Wojick had not gone to his night-watchman's job in the office building downtown. But he saw the hooks on the wall near the door empty of cap and coat.

"For Frankie Thomas," his mother whispered, looking at her son. "His mother is gone again till half the night, and leaves cold cuts. Boy like Frankie to eat cold cuts," she whispered. "You call him, Harry."

"Why can't she learn to speak English?" he asked himself savagely, turning away. "She's been here long enough!"

Harry walked through the short hall and stood under the arch which led into the living room. He saw the frail, black-haired boy with whom he had grown up, sitting in the chair under the lamp. "Hey, Frankie," Harry said. "Come on and eat." Harry whistled shrilly and came back into the kitchen.

He pulled the chair out and held it suspended off the clean, bare floor, his fingers tightening on the wood. There, next to his plate, was the white, square envelope, and atop it, covered by a transparent sheet of thin paper, was the embossed[1] invitation.

Harry looked at his mother, who had her back to him, busy at the stove. He heard Frankie coming through the house and knew it was Frankie's work, *knew* it. He moved the chair at last and sat down and, without touching it, his hands holding his knees, he read the invitation from the faculty of Hamilton High School to an open house in honor of all the students' mothers.

It was for tomorrow.

Harry knew *that*, all right. Had known it for ten days and had kept it secret. He looked up as Frankie sat down across the table.

Harry's mother was sitting between them, and as she handed her son the roast she said, "I asked Frankie maybe he has this invitation, Harry. I heard by Celusik, the grocery man, about this open house. Must be open house for junior, senior mothers." Frankie had skipped a grade.

Harry was busy with the roast. "It's for everyone," he said, watching the roast. "Didn't you get one, Ma?" He turned to his mother. "They mailed them out," Harry said, remembering now that morning when he had waited for the postman on the corner, taken the envelopes from him, searched for the square, white one, and had torn it, scattering the pieces in the empty lot before running home and dropping the rest of the mail in the black metal box beside the door.

"Maybe they make a mistake," his mother said.

She reached for a thick slice of the rye bread she baked herself and held it flat in her left hand. She buttered it completely and thickly and brought it to her mouth, taking a large bite, and Harry wanted to leave the table and this house. He remembered the homes on Maple Heights to which he had been invited, where they called it dinner and ate in a dining room with tablecloths; where George Sidley's mother sat at one end of the table and broke her bread piece by piece, buttering it lightly and eating slowly.

1. **embossed** [em bôsd′]: having letters that are raised to stand out from the surface.

"Frankie's ma got this invitation," Theresa Wojick said, nodding at their guest, who lived with his mother in one of the upstairs apartments of the four-family flat. "How long she got the open house, Frankie?"

"Mother had it," Frankie said. "She—we didn't talk about it."

She turned to Harry, smiling at her son. "You eat, Harry. Big ballplayer must eat good," she said.

Harry ate. The three sat in silence.

Later, while Theresa Wojick set out the dessert plates, Frankie said, "How's practice going, Harry?"

"All right, I guess." He wanted this supper finished.

Theresa Wojick filled the dessert plates with pudding. As she sat down she said to Frankie, "Your ma goes to this open house?"

"I don't know," he answered. "She—well, you know, she's pretty busy. One of my aunts is sick and I think she's going to be with her for a few days. She packed her suitcase when she left today."

"Ma," Harry said.

She set her coffee cup down.

"I wanted to tell you, Ma," he said. "I meant to tell you about it and then I forgot, I guess."

"Easy to forget," she said.

"It wouldn't make any difference anyway, Ma," Harry lied. "We've got that game with Central next week and the coach is worried. He's been working us hard all week. He's got a game for tomorrow. You know, he picks two teams from the squad and we play each other."

"I've got to go," Frankie said. "Thanks very much for supper, Mrs. Wojick."

"You're welcome, Frankie. Here"—she reached across the table—"here is the invitation, Frankie," and she offered it to him.

He held it, shifting it from one hand to the other. "Thanks," he said, moving toward the kitchen door. "Thanks. Thanks." And he was gone.

"I won't be finished until about six o'clock, Ma," Harry said.

She nodded. Harry watched her walking to the sink. "Do you want me to miss practice, Ma?" he asked.

She had her back to him.

Mother and Child Elizabeth Catlett, 1970, cedar, courtesy of the artist

"We'll go next year, Ma. I'll be a regular on the team then. We can go next year," he said, but she didn't turn, nor move, nor did she answer him, and he left the kitchen quickly. He went into the living room and stood before the windows. He tried to blame Frankie and couldn't, and he tried to blame Theresa Wojick and couldn't. He was seldom a liar, but he just didn't want her there with George Sidley's mother and Eric Portland's mother.

Harry heard the water running in the sink and the clatter of dishes, and he went back into the kitchen. He opened the cabinet door, reaching for one of the dish towels his mother had cut from sugar sacks and washed white and soft. She took it from his hand.

"You rest, Harry," his mother said. "Big ball game tomorrow. You must rest up for the ball game." She turned from him to the sink.

"All right," he thought, and now he left the house, going out into the vestibule and then to the rear porch. "Let her wash her own dishes," he thought, and walked out to the sidewalk.

Frankie said, "Hi, Harry." He was leaning against the fence in front of Harry's house. He said, "I didn't want to jam you up, Harry."

"You didn't jam me up."

"That ought to be a pretty good game tomorrow, that intrasquad game," Frankie said. "Think I'll watch it."

"There isn't any intrasquad game," Harry muttered.

"You said—"

"I said. I say a lot of things." He felt the meanness in him. He started to walk away, but Frankie took his arm.

"I've got enough for a movie," Frankie said.

"I'm busy," Harry said, jerking his arm free. He left Frankie there, walking down Glover Street. He passed the corner and went on aimlessly.

When he came home he entered the house through the front door and moved through the living room in darkness, turning into his bedroom. He could see the cracks of light below the bathroom door and heard the water running; he wondered if there was ever a time in this house when the water *wasn't* running. He made it to his bedroom and undressed in the darkness, dropping his clothes on the floor and crawling into the turned-down bed.

"All right," he thought, "this time tomorrow it'll be over." He heard the bathroom door open and his mother moving around the house. He lay still, his eyes closed, his breath coming evenly as he simulated sleep, but the sound of her footsteps faded.

For a bad moment he thought of his ma, saw her again at the kitchen table, but he chased the scene from his mind and went, instead, to baseball, seeing himself leading infield practice, and thus, at last, fell asleep.

The first thing he noticed in the morning was his clothes, arranged neatly on the chair beside the bed, the shoes together on the floor and clean socks across them. He dressed quickly.

The kitchen was deserted. He saw his cornflakes and the orange juice and the milk before his chair, but he stood behind it, gulping the juice. As he set the empty glass on the table his mother came in from the rear porch.

"You didn't eat, Harry," she said.

"I'm late, Ma. I've got a test this morning. I've got to study for the test." He wanted to be out of here now as he turned from the table, saw that her hands were full.

She held the clean, freshly dried sweatshirt and the two pairs of wool socks, and he knew now why the water had been running in the bathroom last night. "For your game today, Harry," she said. "You bring me tonight your dirty stuff."

Harry watched her wrap the bundle and he wanted to kiss her, suddenly. He wanted to put his arms around her and hold her as she tied the bundle carefully with the string she always saved. But he only took the package from her and said thanks, and left.

All the way up to school he promised he'd make it up to her. He'd start tonight. He'd sit in the kitchen with Ma; she liked him there studying while she worked. He'd take her for a walk if she wanted. Saturday and Sunday he was staying home the whole time, that's all.

He came into school on the Livingston Drive side. His locker was on the first floor. He put the package inside, took his books, and slammed the locker shut. The bell sounded for first hour and Harry went to English.

Pete Overholt, the team's catcher, sat behind Harry. As they waited for the tardy bell, he nudged Harry. "Look at the women, man," he whispered. "Look at 'em, Harry!"

Harry looked. Not a girl in the class wore saddle shoes, or blue jeans, or boys' shirts with the sleeves rolled above the elbows. They were in Sunday dresses and suits, and high heels.

"The open house," Pete whispered. "All of them showing off for their mothers."

The tardy bell sounded, and Harry saw Miss Liggett look up from the desk. He wasn't called on during the hour, and afterward, on his way to study hall, he waved to George Sidley, who played third base, and to Bernie Cremmens, the right-fielder. They were both wearing sports jackets and regular shirts, and they wore ties. Harry looked down at his sweater worn over the skivvy shirt. His corduroys were clean, but they were corduroys, and around him, in the study hall, was a sea of gray flannels.

There was only one lunch period today because they had to get the cafeteria ready for the open house. Harry bought a sandwich and a glass of milk. Then he saw that half the guys on the team, sitting at the table they shared every day, were dressed up, too. He sat down in a far corner with two guys he didn't know, ate quickly, and left by the side door so he wouldn't have to pass Sidley and Cremmens and the others.

He went to his locker for his afternoon books. He had only a French class left, because, for today, school was over after fifth hour. He sat half hearing Miss Formanek, gazing out the window until his name was called sharply.

Harry turned to the teacher, his face red, feeling the eyes of the whole class on him as Miss Formanek smiled. "Let's look alive there," said Miss Formanek. "Your mother will find her way, Harry," and she told him the place in the French book.

The bell sounded at last and Harry hurried to his locker. He saw the cafeteria cleared of tables, the floor bare and chairs lining the walls. He saw the huge coffeepots steaming, and then he got his package out and threw his books into the locker and slammed it shut.

He was half running for the door when George Sidley stopped him: "Hey, where you headed for?"

Harry stared at him. "Headed for?" he asked. "Where do you think I'm headed for? Aren't you going to practice?"

"Not me," George grinned. "Coach said anybody who wanted to could be excused. Isn't your mother coming?"

"She had to go downtown," Harry said. "She had to see a doctor. She hasn't been feeling well."

"Hey, that's not good," George said, frowning. Then his face brightened. "Well, hang around anyway. Lots of fun."

Harry shook his head. He swung his left arm. "It feels like it's stiffening up," he said. "Guess I'll work out. See you."

He walked down Livingston Drive toward the baseball field. He crossed the playing area, moving toward the Quonset hut[2] that served as dressing room for the team. There was nobody inside but Art Hughes, the student manager.

"You alone, Harry?" Art asked.

"Yup."

Art turned and opened the doors of the uniform rack. "Anybody that's coming better come quick—that's all I got to say," he announced. "My mother is over at school waiting for me. I'm not keeping her waiting too long."

Harry sat down on the bench before the lockers and unwrapped the package. He pulled his sweater off and he was in his pants and skivvy shirt, standing in his socks on the cement floor when Oscar Anderson walked in. In a few minutes they were joined by Chuck Kellerman, the shortstop, and Mr. Quint, who taught chemistry and was assistant baseball coach.

Mr. Quint came over to the bench. "Look, you fellows; my wife's outside in the car. It seems there are only three of you here. You won't mind if I go back to school, will you?"

---

2. **Quonset hut** [kwon´ sit hut]: prefabricated building made of corrugated metal.

"Go ahead, Mr. Quint," Chuck said.

"I don't want to run out on you," Mr. Quint said. "It's just—well, with only three of you here, there doesn't seem to be much we could do."

"Can I get a ride back?" Art Hughes said. "You guys can check out your own uniforms today."

"Come ahead, Art," Mr. Quint said.

When they were gone, Chuck Kellerman slammed his baseball cap down on the cement floor. "All the way over here for nothing," he said.

He looked at Oscar Anderson. "How about you?" he asked. "Aren't you going to Mamma's Day and eat cookies?"

"Listen; I've got six brothers and sisters and I'm the baby," Oscar said. "My mother's tired of this stuff. I'm going home and get the grass cut, and then I got Saturday for myself."

"How about you, Harry?" Chuck asked.

"How about *you*, wise guy?" Harry said, beginning to tie his shoelaces.

Chuck got up from the bench and reached for a bat. "My mother is dead," he said, and he swung the bat desperately, as though he were hitting a line drive. Then he dropped the bat into the wicker basket. Harry watched him pick up his books and walk to the door and leave without turning to them.

"Will you lock up, Harry?" Oscar asked.

Harry saw his mother in the kitchen, and he reached for his sweater.

"Will you, Harry?"

He remembered the light under the bathroom door and the sound of water as she washed the sweatshirt and the socks.

Mother and Child Jacob Epstein, 1913, marble, 17¼" x 17" x 4", The Museum of Modern Art, New York, gift of A. Conger Goodyear

"HARRY!"

"It isn't too late yet," Harry said. He had his sweater on.

"Are you nuts?" Oscar asked.

He'd call her. He'd use the phone in the principal's office. "See you tomorrow," he said, and he ran out of the Quonset hut. Far off, walking in left-center field, Harry saw Chuck Kellerman, and then he began to run.

He could call her, he thought as he ran, and she could even take a taxi. Just this once a taxi; Pa wouldn't care. Harry knew that. She could get dressed and be up there in half an hour, and he was suddenly breathless with anticipation. He'd wait out in front of the school, on Hamilton Avenue, and help her from the cab and hold her arm and lead her to the front door. He didn't care about the bread any more, or how she talked. She was his ma.

Harry was out of the alley now, running across Livingston Drive. There were cars all around the school, almost like it was graduation night. He cut across the grass, toward the long flight of steps that led up to the second floor. He was gasping for breath when he reached the door.

He stood there a moment, then pulled the heavy door open and stepped into the deserted corridor. There was nobody on the second floor, but from the cafeteria below he heard the muted murmur of a hundred voices.

The principal's door was open. There was a phone in the outer office, an ancient upright that Miss Tibbetts, the principal's secretary, used. Harry took the receiver off the hook, set it on the desk and, holding the upright with his left hand, dialed his home number.

He grinned with excitement thinking of her when she answered. Ma didn't like phones and couldn't hear good on them, but she'd hear this. He could see her listening and her face lighting up, and then, afterward, ordering Pa around to help her, getting the gray dress ready and her coat. She never wore a hat, but let the wind command her hair, and Harry didn't care.

But she didn't answer.

Aloud he said, "Wrong number," but felt the first, tiny stabs of alarm in his chest. He dialed again, slowly now, holding the receiver to his ear, hearing the first ring, the second, the third, the eighth, the ninth, and finally, the operator's voice telling him there was no answer.

He felt the ache in his chest now, and his hands were wet. "Maybe Ma is sick or something," he thought, and he knew who had to take the blame. He dialed the 0 and asked the operator to check the number; maybe the phone was out of order. But all the time he knew it wasn't.

At last he thanked the operator and replaced the receiver and stood listlessly at the desk, wondering what to do. Now he remembered his ma helping him with fractions when he was at Crowley School. He remembered her at graduation, Ma and Pa sitting alone in the back row, and after he had his diploma, when the other guys were bringing their parents up to the front of the auditorium, he had led them out to the hall and home immediately. He remembered her walking over to the skating rink on Inverness Street, standing in a corner beside the fence to watch him skate under the floodlights, careful not to be seen, but he had seen her, all right. Seen her and kept away from that corner.

It seemed to him now, alone in the principal's office, that he had been hiding his ma all his life, and he was sick inside then, with a physical distaste in his mouth. He grimaced with self-hatred, wanting, somehow, to feel a sharper pain, to hurt himself deliberately; and he left the office and almost ran into Mr. Quint and a woman.

"Hello, Harry," Mr. Quint said. "I thought you were practicing."

"I guess not, sir."

"This is my wife, Harry," Mr. Quint said. "Harry Wojick, Emma," he said. "Harry's our first baseman."

Mrs. Quint smiled and shook hands with him.

"Mrs. Quint wants to use the phone," the assistant coach said. "She's worried about our little girl. . . . I'll see you in the cafeteria, dear," he said to his wife.

She nodded, and Mr. Quint took Harry's arm. "Let's get some of those cookies, Harry."

"I can't, sir. My mother isn't there," Harry said.

"Oh, yes. One of the boys told me. She's seeing a doctor. Hasn't been feeling well, eh?"

Harry pulled his arm away. "That's a lie," he said. "I didn't want her to come today."

Mr. Quint started laughing. He put his arm around Harry's shoulders and they walked toward the stairs. "You guys," he said, shaking his head. He looked at Harry. "Do I really look that old, Harry? An old fossil whose leg you all enjoy pulling?"

"What's the difference?" Harry thought. "What difference does it make now?" And his heart leaped as he thought of next year. There'd be an open house next year, but Ma wouldn't go. If she never went anywhere with him, he'd deserve it. If she never talked with him, he had that coming, too. "Just let me get away from Mr. Quint," he thought. Get out of here without trouble and without a fuss. But now they were in the cafeteria, in the midst of mothers and daughters and sons and teachers, and Mr. Quint was pulling him through the mob.

But they got separated and Harry was alone. He wanted to get out quickly now, away from all the laughter and gaiety. He saw Miss Formanek, the French teacher. He saw her wave at him, her finger curved beckoning him. He saw Frankie Thomas standing beside her and the woman between them. He was moving sideways, pushing through the people, and he looked up for Miss Formanek again, and then felt his heart stop. For a long time he remembered his heart stopping dead as he saw the woman in the gray dress.

He thought his legs would give away. His legs were shaking and he was shaking, and he couldn't move until someone pushed him clear and he was standing there before them. He couldn't get his hands free of sweat. He rubbed his hands up and down against the corduroys and looked at his ma.

"I was telling your mother how you were watching for her, Harry. You have a devoted son, Mrs. Wojick," the French teacher said.

Harry saw his ma smile and nod. She was beautiful.

Frankie was wearing a jacket and a tie. How come *he* was dressed up?

"And you're pinch-hitting for Frankie's mother, too," Miss Formanek said. "Frankie was my best student, Mrs. Wojick."

"Frankie's a good boy," Theresa Wojick said.

"They're all good boys," Miss Formanek said, and she excused herself and left them then.

"Ma," Harry said. He had to tell her.

She had her hand in Frankie's arm. She

Cochiti figurine
Laurencita Herrera, pre-1930, polychrome ceramic, 6", Blair Clark photographer, Museum of New Mexico, Santa Fe

was smiling, and her hair was pulled back neat, and she was the loveliest woman he had ever seen. "Ma, I tore up the invitation," he said, and he looked right at her.

"I know," she said. "But Frankie has an invitation. We are two orphans: mother without a son, and son without a mother."

"I'm your son, Ma," Harry said, and saw Frankie slipping away, but his mother held the black-haired boy.

She was wearing white gloves and she looked right at him, and he was more afraid than he had ever been in his life.

"Ma." He held her elbows as she had held his and he didn't drop his eyes. He said, "Please, Ma, I'm your son. Please, Ma, let's get something to eat. There's my coach there. I want to introduce you to my coach."

"Yes," she said, and she smiled at him then, and for him. "Yes," she said, and put one hand through his arm and the other through Frankie's. "Introduce, please, to this coach, my little son."

NORMAN KATKOV

Soon after Norman Katkov's birth in Russia in 1918, his family emigrated to the United States. After attending the University of Minnesota, he served in the army during World War II, and then decided to become a professional writer. Katkov has written a number of books as well as short stories, serials, and articles. He found his niche, however, in writing movie and television scripts—including "The Virginian" and "Hawaiian Eye."

The Writer

RICHARD WILBUR

In her room at the prow of the house
Where light breaks, and the windows are tossed with linden,
My daughter is writing a story.

I pause in the stairwell, hearing
From her shut door a commotion of typewriter keys   5
Like a chain hauled over a gunwale.[1]

Young as she is, the stuff
Of her life is a great cargo, and some of it heavy:
I wish her a lucky passage.

But now it is she who pauses,   10
As if to reject my thought and its easy figure.
A stillness greatens, in which

The whole house seems to be thinking,
And then she is at it again with a bunched clamor
Of strokes, and again is silent.   15

I remember the dazed starling
Which was trapped in that very room, two years ago;
How we stole in, lifted a sash

And retreated, not to affright it;
And how for a helpless hour, through the crack of the door,   20
We watched the sleek, wild dark

And iridescent creature
Batter against the brilliance, drop like a glove
To the hard floor, or the desk-top,

1. **gunwale** [gun ′l]: the upper edge of the side of a ship.

And wait then, humped and bloody,   25
For the wits to try it again; and how our spirits
Rose when, suddenly sure,

It lifted off from a chair-back,
Beating a smooth course for the right window
And clearing the sill of the world.   30

It is always a matter, my darling,
Of life or death, as I had forgotten. I wish
What I wished you before, but harder.

RICHARD WILBUR

Richard Wilbur, born in New York City in 1921, grew up
in a rural area of New Jersey, where he spent a "pleasant and
somewhat solitary boyhood." He wrote his first poem, "That's
Where the Nightingales Wake," when he was eight years old.
A prize-winning poet and a professor, Richard Wilbur
has published numerous collections of his poetry, including *The Mind-Reader* from which the poem "The
Writer" is taken.

Carrying the Clouds Dionisio Blanco, acrylic and oil on canvas, 1989, 45" x 72"

NA TREE

JAMES BERRY

In the hours the hurricane stayed, its presence made every-body older. It made Mr. Bass see that not only people and animals and certain valuables were of most importance to be saved.

From its very buildup the hurricane meant to show it was merciless, unstoppable, and, with its might, changed landscapes.

All day the Jamaican sun didn't come out. Then, ten minutes before, there was a swift shower of rain that raced by and was gone like some urgent messenger-rush of wind. And again everything went back to that quiet, that unnatural quiet. It was as if trees crouched quietly in fear. As if, too, birds knew they should shut up. A thick and low black cloud had covered the sky and shadowed everywhere, and made it seem like night was coming on. And the cloud deep-ened. Its deepening spread more and more over the full stretch of the sea.

The doom-laden afternoon had the atmosphere of Judgment Day for everybody in all the districts about. Everybody knew the hour of disaster was near. Warnings printed in bold lettering had been put up at post offices, police stations, and schoolyard entrances and in clear view on shop walls in village squares.

Carrying children and belongings, people hurried in files and in scattered groups, headed for the big, strong, and safe community buildings. In Canerise Village, we headed for the schoolroom. Loaded with bags and cases, with bundles and lidded baskets, individuals carrying or leading an animal, parents shrieking for children to stay at their heels, we arrived there. And, looking around, anyone would think the whole of Canerise was here in this vast superbarn of a noisy chattering schoolroom.

With violent gusts and squalls the storm broke. Great rushes, huge bulky rushes, of wind struck the building in heavy repeated thuds, shaking it over and over, and carrying on.

Families were huddled together on the floor. People sang, sitting on benches, desks, anywhere there was room. Some people knelt in loud prayer. Among the refugees' noises a goat bleated, a hen fluttered or cackled, a dog whined.

Mr. Jetro Bass was sitting on a soap box. His broad back leaned on the blackboard against the wall. Mrs. Imogene Bass, largely pregnant, looked a midget beside him. Their children were sitting on the floor. The eldest boy, Gustus, sat farthest from his father. Altogether, the children's heads made seven different levels of height around the parents. Mr. Bass forced a reassuring smile. His toothbrush mustache moved about a little as he said, "The storm's bad, chil'run. Really bad. But it'll blow off. It'll spen' itself out. It'll kill itself."

Except for Gustus's, all the faces of the children turned up with subdued fear and looked at their father as he spoke.

"Das true wha' Pappy say," Mrs. Bass said. "The good Lord won' gi' we more than we can bear."

Mr. Bass looked at Gustus. He stretched fully through the sitting children and put a lumpy, blistery hand—though a huge hand—on the boy's head, almost covering it. The boy's clear brown eyes looked straight and unblinkingly into his father's face. "Wha's the matter, bwoy?" his dad asked.

He shook his head. "Nothin', Pappy."

"Wha' mek you say nothin'? I sure somet'ing bodder you, Gustus. You not a bwoy who frighten easy. Is not the hurricane wha' bodder you? Tell Pappy."

"Is nothin'."

"You're a big bwoy now. Gustus—you nearly thirteen. You strong. You very useful fo' you age. You good as mi right han'. I depen' on you. But this afternoon—earlier—in the rush, when we so well push to move befo' storm broke, you couldn' rememba a t'ing! Not one t'ing! Why so? Wha' on you mind? You harborin' t'ings from me, Gustus?"

Gustus opened his mouth to speak, but closed it again. He knew his father was proud of how well he had grown. To strengthen him, he had always given him "last milk" straight from the cow in the mornings. He was thankful. But to him his strength was only proven in the number of innings he could pitch for his cricket team. The boy's lips trembled. What's the good of tellin' when Pappy don' like cricket. He only get vex an' say it's Satan's game for idle hands! He twisted his head and looked away. "I'm harborin' nothin', Pappy."

"Gustus . . ."

At that moment a man called, "Mr. Bass!" He came up quickly. "Got a hymnbook, Mr. Bass? We want you to lead us singing."

The people were sitting with bowed heads, humming a song. As the repressed singing grew louder and louder, it sounded mournful in the room. Mr. Bass shuffled, looking around as if he wished to back out of the suggestion. But his rich voice and singing leadership were too famous. Mrs. Bass already had the hymnbook in her hand, and she pushed it at her husband. He took it and began turning the leaves as he moved toward the center of the room.

Immediately Mr. Bass was surrounded. He started with a resounding chant over the heads of everybody. "Abide[1] wid me; fast fall the eventide. . . ." [2] He joined the singing, but broke off to recite the next line. "The darkness deepen; Lord, wid me, abide. . . ." Again, before the last long-drawn note faded from the deeply stirred voices, Mr. Bass intoned musically, "When odder helpers fail, and comfo'ts flee . . ."

In this manner he fired inspiration into the singing of hymn after hymn. The congregation swelled their throats, and their mixed voices filled the room, pleading to heaven from the depths of their hearts. But the wind outside mocked viciously. It screamed. It whistled. It smashed everywhere up.

1. **abide** [ə bīd′]: stay, remain.
2. **eventide** [ē′ vən tīd]: evening.

Party Time Caribbean Urania Cummings, 1976, oil on canvas, 19" x 25",
Collection of the Cummings Family, photo by M. Lee Fatherree

Mrs. Bass had tightly closed her eyes, singing and swaying in the
center of the children who nestled around her. But Gustus was by
himself. He had his elbows on his knees and his hands blocking his
ears. He had his own worries.

What's the good of Pappy asking all those questions when he
treat him so bad? He's the only one in the family without a pair of
shoes! Because he's a big boy, he don't need anyt'ing an' must do all
the work. He can't stay at school in the evenings an' play cricket
because there's work to do at home. He can't have no outings with

the other children because he has no shoes. An' now when he was to sell his bunch of bananas an' buy shoes so he can go out with his cricket team, the hurricane is going to blow it down.

It was true: the root of the banana was his "navel string." After his birth the umbilical cord was dressed with castor oil and sprinkled with nutmeg and buried, with the banana tree planted over it for him. When he was nine days old, the nana midwife had taken him out into the open for the first time. She had held the infant proudly, and walked the twenty-five yards that separated the house from the kitchen, and at the back showed him his tree. "'Memba when you grow up," her toothless mouth had said, "it's you nable strings feedin' you tree, the same way it feed you from you mudder."

Refuse from the kitchen made the plant flourish out of all proportion. But the rich soil around it was loose. Each time the tree gave a shoot, the bunch would be too heavy for the soil to support; so it crashed to the ground, crushing the tender fruit. This time, determined that his banana must reach the market, Gustus had supported his tree with eight props. And as he watched it night and morning, it had become very close to him. Often he had seriously thought of moving his bed to its root.

Muffled cries, and the sound of blowing noses, now mixed with the singing. Delayed impact of the disaster was happening. Sobbing was everywhere. Quickly the atmosphere became sodden with the wave of weeping outbursts. Mrs. Bass's pregnant belly heaved. Her younger children were upset and cried, "Mammy, Mammy, Mammy. . . ."

Realizing that his family, too, was overwhelmed by the surrounding calamity, Mr. Bass bustled over to them. Because their respect for him bordered on fear, his presence quieted all immediately. He looked around. "Where's Gustus! Imogene . . . where's Gustus!"

"He was 'ere, Pappy," she replied, drying her eyes. "I dohn know when he get up."

Briskly Mr. Bass began combing the schoolroom to find his boy. He asked; no one had seen Gustus. He called. There was no answer. He tottered, lifting his heavy boots over heads, fighting his way to the jalousie.[3] He opened it and his eyes gleamed up and down the road, but saw nothing of the boy. In despair Mr. Bass gave one last thunderous shout: "Gustus!" Only the wind sneered.

By this time Gustus was halfway on the mile journey to their house. The lone figure in the raging wind and shin-deep road flood was tugging, snapping, and pitching branches out of his path. His shirt was fluttering from his back like a boat sail. And a leaf was fastened to his cheek. But the belligerent wind was merciless. It bellowed into his ears and drummed a deafening commotion. As he grimaced and covered his ears, he was forcefully slapped against a coconut tree trunk that lay across the road.

When his eyes opened, his round face was turned up to a festered sky. Above the tormented trees a zinc sheet[4] writhed, twisted, and somersaulted in the tempestuous flurry. Leaves of all shapes and sizes were whirling and diving like attackers around the zinc sheet. As Gustus turned to get up, a bullet drop of rain struck his temple. He shook his head, held grimly to the tree trunk, and struggled to his feet.

Where the road was clear, he edged along the bank. Once, when the wind staggered him, he recovered with his legs wide apart. Angrily he stretched out his hands with clenched fists and shouted, "I almos' hol' you that time . . . come solid like that again an' we fight like man an' man!"

When Gustus approached the river he had to cross, it was flooded and blocked beyond recognition. Pressing his chest against the gritty road bank, the boy closed his weary eyes on the brink of the spating river. The wrecked footbridge had become the harboring fort for all the debris, branches, and monstrous tree trunks which the river swept along its course. The river was still swelling. More accumulation arrived each moment, ramming and pressing the bridge. Under pressure it was cracking and shifting minutely toward a turbulent forty-foot fall.

3. **jalousie** [jal′ ə zē]: a window shade or shutter that keeps out sun and rain.
4. **zinc sheet**: a sheet of blue-white metal; one of its uses is as roofing material.

Gustus had seen it! A feeling of dismay paralyzed him, reminding him of his foolish venture. He scraped his cheek on the bank looking back. But how can he go back? He has no strength to go back. His house is nearer than the school. An' Pappy will only strap him for nothin' . . . for nothin' . . . no shoes, nothin' when the hurricane is gone.

With trembling fingers he tied up the remnants of his shirt. He made a bold step and the wind half lifted him, ducking him in the muddy flood. He sank to his neck. Floating leaves, sticks, coconut husks, dead ratbats, and all manner of feathered creatures and refuse surrounded him. Forest vines under the water entangled him. But he struggled desperately until he clung to the laden bridge and climbed up among leafless branches.

His legs were bruised and bore deep scratches, but steadily he moved up on the slimy pile. He felt like a man at sea, in the heart of a storm, going up the mast of a ship. He rested his feet on a smooth log that stuck to the water-splashed heap like a black torso. As he strained up for another grip, the torso came to life and leaped from under his feet. Swiftly sliding down, he grimly clutched some brambles.

The urgency of getting across became more frightening, and he gritted his teeth and dug his toes into the debris, climbing with maddened determination. But a hard gust of wind slammed the wreck, pinning him like a motionless lizard. For a minute the boy was stuck there, panting, swelling his naked ribs.

He stirred again and reached the top. He was sliding over a breadfruit limb when a flutter startled him. As he looked and saw the clean-head crow and glassy-eyed owl close together, there was a powerful jolt. Gustus flung himself into the air and fell in the expanding water on the other side. When he surfaced, the river had dumped the entire wreckage into the gurgling gully. For once the wind helped. It blew him to land.

Gustus was in a daze when he reached his house. Mud and rotten leaves covered his head and face, and blood caked around a gash on his chin. He bent down, shielding himself behind a tree stump whose white heart was a needly splinter, murdered by the wind.

He could hardly recognize his yard. The terrorized trees that stood were writhing in turmoil. Their thatched house had collapsed like an open umbrella that was given a heavy blow. He looked the other way and whispered, "Is still there! That's a miracle. . . . That's a miracle."

Dodging the wind, he staggered from tree to tree until he got to his own tormented banana tree. Gustus hugged the tree. "My nable string!" he cried. "My nable string! I know you would stan' up to it, I know you would."

The bones of the tree's stalky leaves were broken, and the wind lifted them and harrassed them. And over Gustus's head the heavy fruit swayed and swayed. The props held the tree, but they were squeaking and slipping. And around the plant the roots stretched and trembled, gradually surfacing under loose earth.

With the rags of his wet shirt flying off his back, Gustus was down busily on his knees, bracing, pushing, tightening the props. One by one he was adjusting them until a heavy rush of wind knocked him to the ground. A prop fell on him, but he scrambled to his feet and looked up at the thirteen-hand bunch of bananas. "My good tree," he bawled, "hol' you fruit. . . . Keep it to you heart like a mudder savin' her baby! Don't let the wicked wind t'row you to the groun' . . . even if it t'row me to the groun'. I will not leave you."

But several attempts to replace the prop were futile. The force of the wind against his weight was too much for him. He thought of a rope to lash the tree to anything, but it was difficult to make his way into the kitchen, which, separate from the house, was still standing. The invisible hand of the wind tugged, pushed, and forcefully restrained him. He got down and crawled on his belly into the earth-floor kitchen. As he showed himself with the rope, the wind tossed him, like washing on the line, against his tree.

The boy was hurt! He looked crucified against the tree. The spike of the wind was slightly withdrawn. He fell, folded on the ground. He lay there unconscious. And the wind had no mercy for him. It shoved him, poked him, and molested his clothes like muddy newspaper against the tree.

Hurricane Julio Larraz, 1985, oil on canvas, 48 ¹/₂″ x 79″

As darkness began to move in rapidly, the wind grew more vicious and surged a mighty gust that struck the resisting kitchen. It was heaved to the ground in a rubbled pile. The brave wooden hut had been shielding the banana tree, but in its death fall missed it by inches. The wind charged again and the soft tree gurgled—the fruit was torn from it and plunged to the ground.

The wind was less fierce when Mr. Bass and a searching party arrived with lanterns. Because the bridge was washed away, the hazardous roundabout journey had badly impeded them.

Talks about safety were mockery to the anxious father. Relentlessly he searched. In the darkness his great voice echoed everywhere, calling for his boy. He was wrenching and ripping through the house wreckage

Tropical Landscape Dionisio Blanco,
oil on canvas, 1990, 24 ½" x 50"

when suddenly he vaguely remembered how the boy had
been fussing with the banana
tree. Desperate, the man struggled from the ruins, flagging the
lantern he carried.

The flickering light above
his head showed Mr. Bass the
forlorn and pitiful banana tree.
There it stood, shivering and
twitching like a propped-up
man with lacerated throat and
dismembered head. Half of the
damaged fruit rested on Gustus.
The father hesitated. But when
he saw a feeble wink of the
boy's eyelids, he flung himself
to the ground. His bristly chin
rubbed the child's face while
his unsteady hand ran all over
his body. "Mi bwoy!" he mur-
mured. "Mi hurricane bwoy!
The Good Lord save you. . . .
Why you do this? Why you do
this?"

"I did want buy mi shoes,
Pappy. I . . . I can't go anywhere
'cause I have no shoes. . . . I didn'

go to school outing at the factory. I didn' go to Government House. I didn' go to Ol' Fort in town."

Mr. Bass sank into the dirt and stripped himself of his heavy boots. He was about to lace them to the boy's feet when the onlooking men prevented him. He tied the boots together and threw them over his shoulder.

Gustus's broken arm was strapped to his side as they carried him away. Mr. Bass stroked his head and asked how he felt. Only then grief swelled inside him and he wept.

JAMES BERRY

James Berry was born in 1925 in Jamaica and moved to England when he was twenty-three years old. While leading writing workshops for children in the British school system, he discovered there were very few books that related to his childhood in Jamaica. "In the Caribbean, we were the last outpost of the British Empire," he noted. "No one had reported our stories or the way we saw things." Berry began to write to fill the gap with stories "straight out of my own childhood."

Berry writes both poetry and prose. He feels that more people of all cultures now accept and enjoy the ethnic differences among them. Two notable books by James Berry are *When I Dance: Poems* and *A Thief in the House and Other Stories*.

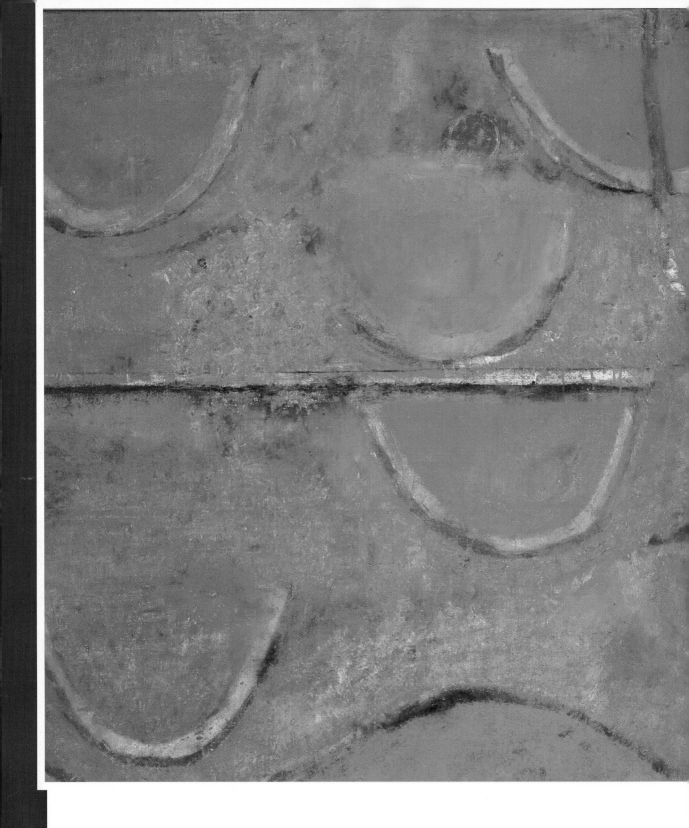

Sandías Rufino Tamayo, 1968,
oil on canvas, 52 x 78",
Collection: Museo Tamayo/INBA

The Taste of Melon

BORDEN DEAL

When I think of the summer I was sixteen, a lot of things come crowding in to be thought about. We had moved just the year before, and sixteen is still young enough that the bunch makes a difference. I had a bunch, all right, but they weren't sure of me yet. I didn't know why. Maybe because I'd lived in town, and my father still worked there instead of farming, like the other fathers did. The boys I knew, even Freddy Gray and J. D., still kept a small distance between us.

Then there was Willadean Wills. I hadn't been much interested in girls before. But I had to admit to myself that I was interested in Willadean. She was my age, nearly as tall as I, and up till the year before, Freddy Gray told me, she had been good at playing Gully Keeper and Ante-Over. But she didn't play such games this year. She was tall and slender, and Freddy Gray and J. D. and I had several discussions about the way she walked. I maintained she was putting it on, but J. D. claimed she couldn't help it. Freddy Gray remarked that she hadn't walked that way last year. He said she'd walked like any other human being. So then I said, put on or not, I liked the way she walked, and then there was a large silence.

It wasn't a comfortable silence, because of Mr. Wills, Willadean's father. We were all afraid of Mr. Wills.

Mr. Wills was a big man. He had bright, fierce eyes under heavy brows and, when he looked down at you, you just withered. The idea of having him angry at one of us was enough to shrivel the soul. All that summer Willadean walked up and down the high road or sat on their front porch in a rocking chair, her dress flared out around her, and not one of us dared do more than say good morning to her.

Mr. Wills was the best farmer in the community. My father said he could drive a stick into the ground and grow a tree out of it. But it wasn't an easy thing with him; Mr. Wills fought the earth when he worked it. When he plowed his fields, you could hear him yelling for a mile. It was as though he dared the earth not to yield him its sustenance.

Above all, Mr. Wills could raise watermelons. Now, watermelons are curious things. Some men can send off for the best watermelon seed, they can plant it in the best ground they own, they can hoe it and tend it with the greatest of care, and they can't raise a melon bigger than your two fists. Other men, like Mr. Wills, can throw seed on the ground, scuff dirt over it, walk off, and leave it and have a crop of the prettiest, biggest melons you ever saw.

Mr. Wills always planted the little field directly behind his barn to watermelons. It ran from the barn to the creek, a good piece of land with just the right sandy soil for melon raising. It seemed as though the melons just bulged up out of the ground for him.

But they were Mr. Wills's melons; he didn't have any idea of sharing them with the boys of the neighborhood. He was fiercer about his melons than anything else; if you just happened to walk close to his melon patch, you'd see Mr. Wills standing and watching you with a glower on his face. And likely as not he'd have his gun under his arm.

Everybody expected to lose a certain quantity of their watermelons to terrapins[1] and a certain quantity to boys. It wasn't considered stealing to sneak into a man's melon patch and judiciously borrow a sample of his raising. You might get a load of salt in the seat of your pants if you were seen, but that was part of the game. You'd be looked down on only if you got malicious and stamped a lot of melons into the ground while you were about it. But Mr. Wills didn't think that way.

That summer I was sixteen Mr. Wills raised the greatest watermelon ever seen in the country. It grew in the very middle of his patch, three times as big as any melon anybody had ever seen. Men came from miles around to look at it. Mr. Wills wouldn't let them go into the melon patch. They had to stand around the edge.

Just like all other daredevil boys in that county, I guess Freddy Gray and J. D. and I had talked idly about stealing that giant watermelon. But we all knew that it was just talk. Not only were we afraid of Mr. Wills and his rages but we knew that Mr. Wills sat in the hayloft window of his barn every night with his shotgun, guarding the melon. It was his seed melon.[2] He meant to plant next year's crop out of that great one, and maybe raise a whole field of them. Mr. Wills was in a frenzy of fear that somebody would steal it. Why, he would rather you stole Willadean than his melon. At least, he didn't guard Willadean with his shotgun.

Every night I could sit on our front porch and see Mr. Wills sitting up there in the window of his hayloft, looking fiercely out over his melon patch. I'd sit there by the hour and watch him, the shotgun cradled in his arm, and feel the tremors of fear and excitement chasing up and down my spine.

"Look at him," my father would say. "Scared to death somebody will steal his seed melon. Wouldn't anybody steal a man's seed melon."

"He ought to be in the house taking care of that wife of his," my mother would say tartly. "She's been poorly all year."

---

1. **terrapins** [terʹ ə pinz]: edible North American turtles that live in fresh water or tidewater.
2. **seed melon**: a melon whose seeds are planted for the next crop.

You hardly ever saw Mrs. Wills. She was a wraith of a woman, pale as a butter bean. Sometimes she would sit for an hour or two on their porch in the cool of the day. They didn't visit back and forth with anybody, though.

"There's Willadean," my father would say mildly.

My mother would make a funny kind of sound that meant disgust. "He cares more about that seed melon than he does his wife," she'd say. "I wish somebody *would* steal it. Maybe then—"

"Helen," my father would say, chiding, "you shouldn't even think of such a thing."

About the time the great watermelon was due to come ripe, there was a night of a full moon. J. D. and Freddy Gray and I had decided we'd go swimming in the creek, so I left the house when the moon rose and went to meet them. The moon floated up into the sky and made everything almost as bright as day, but at the same time softer and gentler than ever daylight could be. It was the kind of night when you feel as though you can do anything in the world, even boldly ask Willadean Wills for a date. On a night like that, you couldn't help feel she'd gladly accept.

"Boy, what a moon!" J. D. said when I met Freddy Gray and him.

"Wouldn't you like to take old Willadean out on a night like this?" Freddy said.

We scoffed at him, but secretly in our hearts we knew how he felt. We were getting old enough to think that that sort of thing might be a lot more fun than going swimming in the moonlight.

As I said before, I was a part of the bunch. J. D. and Freddy Gray were my good friends. But because I was still new, there were certain things and certain feelings where I was left out. This was one of them; they were afraid, because I was more of a stranger to Willadean, that she might like the idea of dating me better than she did either of them. This was all way down under the surface, because none of us had admitted to ourselves that we wanted to be Willadean's boy friend. But far down though it was, I could feel it, and they could feel it.

"I wish I had a newspaper," I said then. "I'll bet you could read it in this moonlight."

We had reached the swimming hole in the creek, and we began shucking off our clothes. We were all excited by the moonlight, yelling at one another and rushing to be

American Still Life anonymous, c. 1870, oil on canvas, Private Collection, courtesy Samuel Herrup Antiques

first into the water. Freddy Gray made it first, J.D. and I catapulting in right behind him. The water was cold, and the shock of it struck a chill into us. But we got rid of it by a water fight and then we were all right.

We climbed out finally, to rest, and sat on the bank. That big old moon sailed serenely overhead, climbing higher into the sky, and we lay on our backs to look up at it.

"Old Man Wills won't have to worry about anybody stealing his

The Taste of Melon   **71**

melon tonight, anyway," Freddy Gray said. "Wouldn't anybody dare try it, bright as day like it is."

"He's not taking any chances," J. D. said. "I saw him sitting up in that hayloft when I came by, his shotgun loaded with buckshot. That melon is as safe as it would be in the First National Bank."

"Shucks," I said in a scoffing voice, "he ain't got buckshot in that gun. He's just got a load of salt, like anybody else guarding a watermelon patch."

Freddy Gray sat upright, looking at me. "Don't kid yourself, son," he said loftily. "He told my daddy that he had it loaded with double-ought buckshot."[3]

"Why," I said, "that would kill a man."

"That's what he's got in mind," Freddy Gray said, "if anybody goes after that seed melon."

It disturbed me more than it should have. After all, I'd never had it in mind to try for the melon, had I? "I don't believe it," I said flatly. "He wouldn't kill anybody over a watermelon. Even a seed melon like that one."

"Old Man Wills would," J. D. said.

Freddy Gray was still watching me. "What's got you into such a swivet?"

he said. "You weren't planning on going after that melon yourself?"

"Well, yes," I said. "As a matter of fact, I was."

There was a moment of respectful silence. Even from me. I hadn't known I was going to say those words. To this day I don't know why I said them. It was all mixed up with Willadean and the rumor of Mr. Wills having his gun loaded with double-ought buckshot and the boys still thinking of me as an outsider. It surged up out of me—not the idea of making my name for years to come by such a deed, but the feeling that there was a rightness in defying the world and Mr. Wills.

Mixed up with it all there came into my mouth the taste of watermelon. I could taste the sweet red juices oozing over my tongue, feel the delicate threaded redness of the heart as I squeezed the juices out of it.

I stood up. "As a matter of fact," I said, "I'm going after it right now."

"Wait a minute," J. D. said in alarm. "You can't do it on a moonlight night like this. It's 200 yards from the creek bank to that melon. He'll see you for sure."

"Yeah," Freddy Gray said, "wait until a dark night. Wait until—"

---

3. **double-ought buckshot** [dubl ôt buk′shot]: small lead ball or shot fired from a shotgun; double-ought (00) refers to the size of the shot.

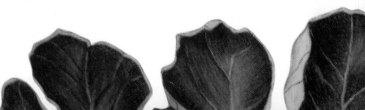

"Anybody could steal it on a dark night," I said scornfully. "I'm going to take it right out from under his nose. Tonight."

I began putting on my clothes. My heart was thudding in my chest. I didn't taste watermelon any more; I tasted fear. But it was too late to stop now. Besides, I didn't want to stop.

We dressed silently, and I led the way up the creek bank. We came opposite the watermelon patch and ducked down the bank. We pushed through the willows on the other side and looked toward the barn. We could see Mr. Wills very plainly. The gun was cradled in his arms, glinting from the moonlight.

"You'll never make it," J. D. said in a quiet, fateful voice. "He'll see you before you're six steps away from the creek."

"You don't think I mean to walk, do you?" I said.

I pushed myself out away from them, on my belly in the grass that grew up around the watermelon hills. I was absolutely flat, closer to the earth than I thought it was possible to get. I looked back once, to see their white faces watching me out of the willows.

I went on, stopping once in a while to look cautiously up toward the barn. He was still there, still quiet. I met a terrapin taking a bite out of a small melon. Terrapins love watermelon, better than boys do. I touched him on the shell and whispered, "Hello, brother," but he didn't acknowledge my greeting. He just drew into his shell. I went on, wishing I were equipped like a terrapin for the job, outside as well as inside.

It seemed to take forever to reach the great melon in the middle of the field. With every move, I expected Mr. Wills to see me. Fortunately the grass was high enough to cover me. At last the melon loomed up before me, deep green in the moonlight, and I gasped at the size of it. I'd never seen it so close.

I lay still for a moment, panting. I didn't have the faintest idea how to get it out of the field. Even if I'd stood up, I couldn't have lifted it by myself. A melon is the slipperiest, most cumbersome object in the world. And this was the largest I'd ever seen. It was not a long melon, but a fat round one. Besides, I didn't dare stand up.

For five minutes I didn't move. I lay there, my nostrils breathing up the smell of the earth and the musty smell of the watermelon vines, and I wondered why I was out here in the middle of all that moonlight on such a venture. There was more to it than just bravado. I was proving something to

The Taste of Melon 73

myself—and to Mr. Wills and Willadean.

I thought of a tempting way out then. I would carve my name into the deep greenness of the melon. Mr. Wills would see it the next morning when he inspected the melon, and he would know that I could have stolen it if I'd wanted to. But no—crawling to the melon wasn't the same thing as actually taking it.

I reached one hand around the melon and found the stem. I broke the tough stem off close against the smooth roundness, and I was committed. I looked toward the barn again. All quiet. I saw Mr. Wills stretch and yawn, and his teeth glistened; the moon was that bright and I was that close.

I struggled around behind the melon and shoved at it. It rolled over sluggishly, and I pushed it again. It was hard work, pushing it down the trough my body had made through the grass. Dust rose up around me, and I wanted to sneeze. My spine was crawling, expecting a shot. Surely he'd see that the melon was gone out of its accustomed space.

It took about a hundred years to push that melon out of the field. I say that advisedly because I felt that

much older when I finally reached the edge. With the last of my strength I shoved it into the willows and collapsed. I was still lying on the edge of the field.

"Come on," Freddy Gray said, his voice pleading. "He's—"

I couldn't move. I turned my head. He was standing up to stretch and yawn to his content, and then he sat down again. By then I was rested enough to move again. I snaked into the willows, and they grabbed me.

"You did it!" they said. "By golly, you did it!"

There was no time to bask in their admiration and respect. "Let's get it on out of here," I said. "We're not safe yet."

We struggled the melon across the creek and up the bank. We started toward the swimming hole. It took all three of us to carry it, and it was hard to get a grip. J. D. and Freddy Gray carried the ends, while I walked behind the melon, grasping the middle. We stumbled and thrashed[4] in our hurry, and we nearly dropped it three or four times. It was the most difficult object I'd ever tried to carry in my life.

At last we reached the swimming hole and sank down, panting. But not for long; the excitement was too

---

4. **thrashed** [thrashed]: moved violently.

strong in us. Freddy Gray reached out a hand and patted the great melon.

"By golly," he said, "there it is. All ours."

"Let's bust it and eat it before somebody comes," J. D. said.

"Wait a minute," I said. "This isn't just any old melon. This is old man Will's seed melon, and it deserves more respect than to be busted open with a fist. I'm going to cut it."

I took out my pocketknife and looked at it. It was small, and the melon was big. We really needed a butcher knife. But when the little knife penetrated the thick green rind, the melon split of itself, perfectly down the middle. There was a ragged, silken, tearing sound, and it lay open before us.

The heart meat, glistening with sweet moisture, was grained with white sugar specks. I tugged at it with two fingers, and a great chunk of the meat came free. I put it into my mouth and closed my eyes. The melon was still warm from the day's sun. Just as in my anticipation, I felt the juice trickle into my throat, sweet and seizing. I had never tasted watermelon so delicious.

The two boys were watching me savor the first bite. I opened my eyes. "Dive in," I said graciously. "Help yourselves."

We gorged ourselves until we were heavy. Even then, we had still only eaten the heart meat, leaving untouched more than we had consumed. We gazed with sated eyes at the leftover melon, still good meat peopled with a multitude of black seeds.

"What are we going to do with it?" I said.

"There's nothing we can do," J. D. said. "I can just see us taking a piece of this melon home for the folks."

"It's eat it or leave it," Freddy Gray said.

We were depressed suddenly. It was such a waste, after all the struggle and danger, that we could not eat every bite. I stood up, not looking at the two boys, not looking at the melon.

"Well," I said. "I guess I'd better get home."

"But what about this?" J. D. said, motioning toward the melon.

I kicked half the melon, splitting it in three parts. I stamped one of the chunks under my foot. Then I set methodically to work, destroying the rest of the melon. The boys watched me silently until I picked up a chunk of rind and threw it at them. Then they swept into the destruction also, and we were laughing again. When we stopped, only the battered rinds

Cherry Stand Wayne Thiebaud, 1963, oil on canvas, The Collection of Mr. and Mrs. Graham Gund, Cambridge, MA

were left, the meat muddied on the ground, the seed scattered.

We stood silent, looking at one another. "There was nothing else to do," I said. They nodded solemnly.

But the depression went with us toward home. I did not feel triumph or victory, as I had expected, though I knew that tonight's action had brought me closer to my friends than I had ever been before.

"Where have you been?" my

father asked as I stepped up on the porch. He was sitting in his rocker.

"Swimming," I said.

I looked toward Mr. Wills's barn. The moon was still high and bright, but I could not see him. My breath caught in my throat when I saw him in the field, walking toward the middle. I stood stiffly, watching him. He reached the place where the melon should have been. I saw him hesitate, looking around; then he bent, and I knew he was looking at the depression in the earth where the melon had lain. He straightened, a great, strangled cry tearing out of his throat. It chilled me deep down and all the way through, like the cry of a wild animal.

My father, startled by the sound, jerked himself out of the chair. He turned in time to see Mr. Wills lift the shotgun over his head and hurl it from him, his voice crying out again in a terrible, surging yell of pain and anger.

"Lord, what's the matter?" my father said.

Mr. Wills was tearing up and down the melon patch, and I was puzzled by his actions. Then I saw; he was destroying every melon in the patch. He was breaking them open with his feet, silent now, concentrating on his frantic destruction. I was horrified by the awful sight, and my stomach moved sickly.

My father stood for a moment, watching Mr. Wills; then he jumped off the porch and ran toward him. I followed him. I saw Mrs. Wills and Willadean huddled together in the kitchen doorway. My father ran into the melon patch and caught Mr. Wills by the arm.

"What's come over you?" he said. "What's the matter, man?"

Mr. Wills struck his grip away. "They've stolen my seed melon," he yelled. "They took it right out from under me."

My father grabbed him with both arms. He was a brave man, for he was smaller than Mr. Wills, and Mr. Wills looked insane with anger, his teeth gripped over his lower lip, his eyes gleaming furiously. Mr. Wills shoved my father away, and struck him with his fist. My father went down into the dirt. Mr. Wills didn't seem to notice. He went back to his task of destruction, raging up and down the field, stamping melons large and small.

My father got up and began to chase him. But he didn't have a chance. Every time he got close, Mr. Wills would sweep his great arm and knock him away again. At last Mr. Wills stopped of his own accord. He was standing on the place where the great melon had grown. His chest

The Taste of Melon   77

was heaving with great sobs of breath. He gazed about him at the destruction he had wrought, but I don't think that he saw it.

"They stole my seed melon," he said. His voice was quieter now than I had ever heard it. I had not believed such quietness was in him. "They got it away, and now it's gone."

I saw that tears stood on his cheeks, and I couldn't look at him any more. I'd never seen a grown man cry, crying in such strength.

"I had two plans for that melon," he told my father. "Mrs. Wills has been poorly all the spring, and she dearly loves the taste of melon. It was her melon for eating, and my melon for planting. She would eat the meat, and next spring I would plant the seeds for the greatest melon crop in the world. Every day she would ask me if the great seed melon was ready yet."

I looked toward the house. I saw the two women, the mother and the daughter, standing there. I couldn't bear any more. I fled out of the field toward the sanctuary of my house. I ran past my mother, standing on the porch, and went into my room.

I didn't sleep that night. I heard my father come in, heard the low-voiced conversation with my mother, heard them go to bed. I lay wide-eyed and watched the moon through the window as it slid slowly down the sky and at last brought welcome darkness into the world.

I don't know all the things I thought that night. Mostly it was about the terrible thing I had committed so lightly, out of pride and out of being sixteen years old and out of wanting to challenge the older man, the man with the beautiful daughter.

That was the worst of all, that I had done it so lightly, with so little thought of its meaning. In that country and in that time, watermelon stealing was not a crime. It was tolerated, laughed about. The men told great tales of their own watermelon-stealing days, how they'd been set on by dogs and peppered with salt-loaded shotgun shells. Watermelon raiding was a game, a ritual of defiance and rebellion by young males. I could remember my own father saying, "No melon tastes as sweet as a stolen one," and my mother laughing and agreeing.

But stealing this great seed melon from a man like Mr. Wills lay outside the safe magic of the tacit understanding between man and boy. And I knew that it was up to me, at whatever risk, to repair as well as I could the damage I had done.

When it was daylight I rose from my bed and went out into the fresh world. It would be hot later on; but now the air was dew-cool and fragrant. I had found a paper sack in the kitchen, and I carried it in my hand as I walked toward the swimming hole. I stopped there and looked down at the wanton waste we had made of the part of the melon we had not been able to eat. It looked as though Mr. Wills had been stamping here too.

I kneeled down on the ground, opened the paper sack and began picking up the black seeds. They were scattered thickly, still stringy with watermelon pulp, and soon my hands were greasy with them. I kept on doggedly, searching out every seed I could find, until at the end I had to crawl over the ground, seeking for the last ones.

They nearly filled the paper sack. I went back to the house.

By the time I reached it, the sun and my father had risen. He was standing on the porch.

"What happened to you last night?" he said. "Did you get so frightened you had to run home? It was frightening to watch him, I'll admit that."

"Father," I said, "I've got to go talk to Mr. Wills. Right now. I wish you would come with me."

He stopped, watching me. "What's the matter?" he said. "Did you steal that seed melon of his?"

"Will you come with me?" I said.

His face was dark and thoughtful. "Why do you want me?"

"Because I'm afraid he'll shoot me," I said. My voice didn't tremble much, but I couldn't keep it all out.

"Then why are you going?" he said.

"Because I've got to," I said.

My father watched me for a moment. "Yes," he said quietly, "I guess you do." He came down the steps and stood beside me. "I'll go with you," he said.

We walked the short distance between our house and his. Though it was so near, I had never been in his yard before. I felt my legs trembling as I went up the brick walk and stood at the bottom of the steps, the paper sack in my hand. I knocked on the porch floor, and Willadean came to the screen door.

I did not look at her. "I want to talk to your father."

She stared at me for a moment,

then she disappeared. In a moment Mr. Wills appeared in the doorway. His face was marked by the night, his cheeks sunken, his mouth bitten in. He stared at me absent-mindedly, as though I were only a speck in his thinking.

"What do you want, boy?" he said.

I felt my teeth grit against the words I had to say. I held out the paper bag. "Mr. Wills," I said, "here are the seeds from your seed melon. That's all I could bring back."

I could feel my father standing quietly behind me. Willadean was standing in the doorway, watching. I couldn't take my eyes away from Mr. Wills's face.

"Did you steal it?"

"Yes, sir," I said.

He advanced to the edge of the porch. The shotgun was standing near the door, and I expected him to reach for it. Instead he came toward me, a great, powerful man, and leaned down to me.

Watermelon in Blue-bordered Dish
anonymous, c. 1840, Abby Aldrich Rockefeller Folk Art Center, Williamsburg, VA

"Why did you steal it?" he said.

"I don't know," I said.

"Didn't you know it was my seed-melon?"

"Yes, sir," I said. "I knew it."

He straightened up again and

his eyes were beginning to gleam. I wanted to run, but I couldn't move.

"And my sick wife hungered for the taste of that melon," he said. "Not for herself, like I thought. But to invite the whole neighborhood in for a slice of it. She knew I wouldn't ever think of anything like that myself. She hungered for that."

I hung my head. "I'm sorry," I said.

He stopped still then, watching me. "So you brought me the seeds," he said softly. "That's not much, boy."

I lifted my head. "It was all I could think to do," I said. "The melon is gone. But the seeds are next year. That's why I brought them to you."

"But you ruined this year," he said.

"Yes, sir," I said. "I ruined this year."

I couldn't look at him any more. I looked at Willadean standing behind him. Her eyes were a puzzle, watching me, and I couldn't tell what she was thinking or feeling.

"I'm about as ashamed of myself last night as you are of yourself," Mr. Wills said. He frowned at me with his heavy brows. "You ruined the half of it, and I ruined the other. We're both to blame, boy. Both to blame."

It seemed there ought to be something more for me to say. I searched for it in my mind and discovered only the thought that I had found this morning in the gray light of dawning.

"The seeds are next year," I said. I looked at him humbly. "I'll help you plant them, Mr. Wills. I'll work hard."

Mr. Wills looked at my father for the first time. There was a small, hard smile on his face; his eyes didn't look as fierce as before.

"A man with a big farm like mine needs a son," he said. "But Willadean here was all the good Lord saw fit to give me. Sam, I do wish I had me a boy like that."

He came close to me then, put his hand on my shoulder. "We can't do anything about this year," he said. "But we'll grow next year, won't we? We'll grow it together."

"Yes, sir," I said.

I looked past him at Willadean, and her eyes were smiling too. I felt my heart give a great thump in my chest.

"And you don't have to offer the biggest melon in the world to get folks to come visiting," I blurted. "Why, I'll set on the porch with Willadean any time."

Mr. Wills and my father burst out laughing. Willadean was blushing red in the face. But somehow she didn't look mad. Flustered, I began to beat a retreat toward the gate. Then I stopped, and looked back at Mr. Wills. I couldn't leave yet.

"Can I ask you one thing, Mr. Wills?" I said.

He stopped laughing, and there was no fierceness in his voice. "Anything you want to, boy," he said.

"Well, I just wanted to know," I said. "Was there double-ought buckshot in that gun?"

He reached around and picked up the gun. He unbreeched it and took out a shell. He broke the shell in his strong fingers and poured the white salt out into his palm.

"You see?" he said.

"Yes, sir," I said, taking a deep breath. "I see."

I went on then, and the next year started that very day.

B O R D E N   D E A L

Borden Deal was born in Pontotoc, Mississippi, in 1922. When he was a young man, at the end of the Depression, he "beat around the country," working for a circus, on a showboat, and in the Civilian Conservation Corps. He started writing while working in Washington, D.C., for the United States Department of Labor. He did not publish anything, however, until he left the Navy and entered the University of Alabama.

Deal did graduate work in Mexico and then supported his writing with a series of odd jobs. A popular story that reflects his southern background is "Antaeus," about a farm boy transplanted to a city.

The Medicine Bag

VIRGINIA DRIVING HAWK SNEVE

Detail from
Medicine Pouch,
Sioux

My kid sister Cheryl and I always bragged about our Sioux[1] grandpa, Joe Iron Shell. Our friends, who had always lived in the city and only knew about Indians from movies and TV, were impressed by our stories. Maybe we exaggerated and made Grandpa and the reservation sound glamorous, but when we'd return home to Iowa after our yearly summer visit to Grandpa, we always had some exciting tale to tell.

We always had some authentic Sioux article to show our listeners. One year Cheryl had new moccasins that Grandpa had made. On another visit he gave me a small, round, flat, rawhide drum that was decorated with a

1. **Sioux** [sü]: member of a Native American people of the northern United States and southern Canada.

Brulé Sioux with Travois
John Anderson, c. 1900, black
and white photo, Nebraska
State Historical Society

painting of a warrior riding a horse. He taught me a real Sioux chant to sing while I beat the drum with a leather-covered stick that had a feather on the end. Man, that really made an impression.

We never showed our friends Grandpa's picture. Not that we were ashamed of him, but because we knew that the glamorous tales we told didn't go with the real thing. Our friends would have laughed at the picture, because Grandpa wasn't tall and stately like TV Indians. His hair wasn't in braids, but hung in stringy, gray strands on his neck, and he was old. He was our great-grandfather, and he didn't live in a tipi, but all by himself in a part log, part tar-paper shack on the Rosebud Reservation in South Dakota. So when Grandpa came to visit us, I was so ashamed and embarrassed I could've died.

There are a lot of yippy poodles and other fancy little dogs in our neighborhood, but they usually barked singly at the mailman from the safety of their own yards. Now it sounded as if a whole pack of mutts were barking together in one place.

I got up and walked to the curb to see what the commotion was. About a block away I saw a crowd of little kids yelling, with the dogs yipping and growling around someone who was walking down the middle of the street.

I watched the group as it slowly came closer and saw that in the center of the strange procession was a man wearing a tall black hat. He'd pause now and then to peer at something in his hand and then at the houses on either side of the street. I felt cold and hot at the same time as I recognized the man. "Oh, no!" I whispered. "It's Grandpa!"

I stood on the curb, unable to move even though I wanted to run and hide. Then I got mad when I saw how the yippy dogs were growling and nipping at the old man's baggy pant legs and how wearily he poked them away with his cane. "Stupid mutts," I said as I ran to rescue Grandpa.

When I kicked and hollered at the dogs to get away, they put their tails between their legs and scattered. The kids ran to the curb where they watched me and the old man.

"Grandpa," I said and felt pretty dumb when my voice cracked. I reached for his beat-up old tin suitcase, which was tied shut with a rope. But he set it down right in the street and shook my hand.

"*Hau, Takoza,*[2] Grandchild," he greeted me formally in Sioux.

All I could do was stand there with the whole neighborhood watching and shake the hand of the leather-brown old man. I saw how his gray hair straggled from under his big black hat, which had a drooping feather in its crown. His rumpled black suit hung like a sack over his stooped frame. As he shook my hand, his coat fell open to expose a bright red satin shirt with a beaded bolo tie[3] under the collar. His get-up wasn't out of place on the reservation, but it sure was here, and I wanted to sink right through the pavement.

"Hi," I muttered with my head down. I tried to pull my hand away when I felt his bony hand trembling, and looked up to see

2. *Hau, Takoza* [häü tä kō′ zä]
3. *bolo tie* [bō′ lo tī]: string tie, with decorated slide.

fatigue in his face. I felt like crying. I couldn't think of anything to say so I picked up Grandpa's suitcase, took his arm, and guided him up the driveway to our house.

Mom was standing on the steps. I don't know how long she'd been watching, but her hand was over her mouth and she looked as if she couldn't believe what she saw. Then she ran to us.

"Grandpa," she gasped. "How in the world did you get here?"

She checked her move to embrace Grandpa and I remembered that such a display of affection is unseemly to the Sioux and would embarrass him.

"*Hau,* Marie," he said as he shook Mom's hand. She smiled and took his other arm.

As we supported him up the steps, the door banged open and Cheryl came bursting out of the house. She was all smiles and was so obviously glad to see Grandpa that I was ashamed of how I felt.

"Grandpa!" she yelled happily. "You came to see us!"

Grandpa smiled, and Mom and I let go of him as he stretched out his arms to my ten-year-old sister, who was still young enough to be hugged.

"*Wicincala,*[4] little girl," he greeted her and then collapsed.

He had fainted. Mom and I carried him into her sewing room, where we had a spare bed.

After we had Grandpa on the bed, Mom stood there helplessly patting his shoulder.

"Shouldn't we call the doctor, Mom?" I suggested, since she didn't seem to know what to do.

"Yes," she agreed with a sigh. "You make Grandpa comfortable, Martin."

I reluctantly moved to the bed. I knew Grandpa wouldn't want to have Mom undress him, but I didn't want to, either. He was so skinny and frail that his coat slipped off easily. When I loosened his tie and opened his shirt collar, I felt a small leather pouch that hung from a thong around his neck. I left it alone and moved to remove

_____

4. *Wicincala* [wē chēn′ chä lä]

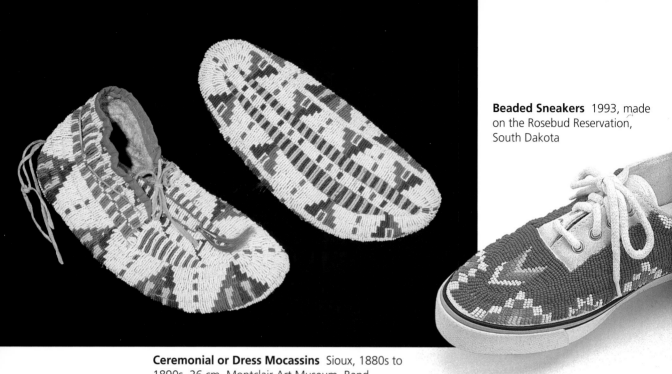

Beaded Sneakers 1993, made on the Rosebud Reservation, South Dakota

Ceremonial or Dress Mocassins Sioux, 1880s to 1890s, 26 cm, Montclair Art Museum, Rand Collection

his boots. The scuffed old cowboy boots were tight, and he moaned as I put pressure on his legs to jerk them off.

I put the boots on the floor and saw why they fit so tight. Each one was stuffed with money. I looked at the bills that lined the boots and started to ask about them, but Grandpa's eyes were closed again.

Mom came back with a basin of water. "The doctor thinks Grandpa is suffering from heat exhaustion," she explained as she bathed Grandpa's face. Mom gave a big sigh, "Oh, *hinh*,[5] Martin. How do you suppose he got here?"

We found out after the doctor's visit. Grandpa was angrily sitting up in bed while Mom tried to feed him some soup.

"Tonight you let Marie feed you, Grandpa," spoke my dad, who had gotten home from work just as the doctor was leaving. "You're not really sick," he said as he gently pushed Grandpa back against the pillows. "The doctor said you just got too tired and hot after your long trip."

Grandpa relaxed, and between sips of soup, he told us of his journey. Soon after our visit to him, Grandpa decided that he would like to see

5. *Oh, hinh* [ō hēn]

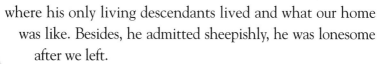

where his only living descendants lived and what our home was like. Besides, he admitted sheepishly, he was lonesome after we left.

I knew everybody felt as guilty as I did—especially Mom. Mom was all Grandpa had left. So even after she married my dad, who's a white man and teaches in the college in our city, and after Cheryl and I were born, Mom made sure that every summer we spent a week with Grandpa.

I never thought that Grandpa would be lonely after our visits, and none of us noticed how old and weak he had become. But Grandpa knew, and so he came to us. He had ridden on buses for two and a half days. When he arrived in the city, tired and stiff from sitting for so long, he set out, walking, to find us.

He had stopped to rest on the steps of some building downtown, and a policeman found him. The cop, according to Grandpa, was a good man who took him to the bus stop and waited until the bus came and told the driver to let Grandpa out at Bell View Drive. After Grandpa got off the bus, he started walking again. But he couldn't see the house numbers on the other side when he walked on the sidewalk, so he walked in the middle of the street. That's when all the little kids and dogs followed him.

I knew everybody felt as bad as I did. Yet I was so proud of this 86-year-old man, who had never been away from the reservation, having the courage to travel so far alone.

"You found the money in my boots?" he asked Mom.

"Martin did," she answered, and roused herself to scold. "Grandpa, you shouldn't have carried so much money. What if someone had stolen it from you?"

Grandpa laughed. "I would've known if anyone tried to take the boots off my feet. The money is what I've saved for a long time—a hundred dollars—for my funeral. But you take it now to buy groceries so that I won't be a burden to you while I am here."

"That won't be necessary, Grandpa," Dad said. "We are honored to have you with us, and you will never be a burden. I am only sorry that we never thought to bring you home with us this summer and spare you the discomfort of a long trip."

Grandpa was pleased. "Thank you," he answered. "But do not feel bad that you didn't bring me with you, for I would not have come then. It was not time." He said this in such a way that no one could argue with him. To Grandpa and the Sioux, he once told me, a thing would be done when it was the right time to do it, and that's the way it was.

"Also," Grandpa went on, looking at me, "I have come because it is soon time for Martin to have the medicine bag."

We all knew what that meant. Grandpa thought he was going to die, and he had to follow the tradition of his family to pass the medicine bag, along with its history, to the oldest male child.

"Even though the boy," he said still looking at me, "bears a white man's name, the medicine bag will be his."

I didn't know what to say. I had the same hot and cold feeling that I had when I first saw Grandpa in the street. The medicine bag was the dirty leather pouch I had found around his neck. "I could never wear such a thing," I almost said aloud. I thought of having my friends see it in gym class, or at the swimming pool, and could imagine the smart things they would say. But I just swallowed hard and took a step toward the bed. I knew I would have to take it.

But Grandpa was tired. "Not now, Martin," he said, waving his hand in dismissal. "It is not time. Now I want sleep."

So that's how Grandpa came to be with us for two months. My friends kept asking to come see the old man, but I put them off. I told myself that I didn't want them laughing at Grandpa. But even as I made excuses, I knew it wasn't Grandpa that I was afraid they'd laugh at.

Nothing bothered Cheryl about bringing her friends to see Grandpa. Every day after school started, there'd be a crew of giggling little girls or round-eyed little boys crowded around the old man on the patio, where he'd gotten in the habit of sitting every afternoon.

Grandpa would smile in his gentle way and patiently answer their questions, or he'd tell them stories of brave warriors, ghosts, animals; and the kids listened in awed silence. Those little guys thought Grandpa was great.

Finally, one day after school, my friends came home with me because nothing I said stopped them. "We're going to see the great Indian of Bell View Drive," said Hank, who was supposed to be my best friend. "My brother has seen him three times so he oughta be well enough to see us."

When we got to my house, Grandpa was sitting on the patio. He had on his red shirt, but today he also wore a fringed leather vest that was decorated with beads. Instead of his usual cowboy boots, he had solidly beaded moccasins on his feet that stuck out of his black trousers. Of course, he had his old black hat on—he was seldom without it. But it had been brushed, and the feather in the beaded headband was proudly erect, its tip a brighter white. His hair lay in silver strands over the red shirt collar.

I stared just as my friends did, and I heard one of them murmur, "Wow!"

Grandpa looked up, and, when his eyes met mine, they twinkled as if he were laughing inside. He nodded to me, and my face got all hot. I could tell that he had known all along I was afraid he'd embarrass me in front of my friends.

"*Hau, hoksilas,*[6] boys," he greeted and held out his hand.

My buddies passed in a single file and shook his hand as I introduced them. They were so polite I almost laughed. "How, there, Grandpa," and even a "How-do-you-do, sir."

"You look fine, Grandpa," I said as the guys sat on the lawn chairs or on the patio floor.

"*Hanh,*[7] yes," he agreed. "When I woke up this morning, it seemed the right time to dress in the good clothes. I knew that my grandson would be bringing his friends."

6. *Hau, hoksilas* [häü hōk sēʹ läs]
7. *Hanh* [hän]

"You guys want some lemonade or something?" I offered. No one answered. They were listening to Grandpa as he started telling how he'd killed the deer from which his vest was made.

Grandpa did most of the talking while my friends were there. I was so proud of him and amazed at how respectfully quiet my buddies were. Mom had to chase them home at supper time. As they left, they shook Grandpa's hand again and said to me.

"Martin, he's really great!"

"Yeah, man! Don't blame you for keeping him to yourself."

"Can we come back?"

But after they left, Mom said, "No more visitors for a while, Martin. Grandpa won't admit it, but his strength hasn't returned. He likes having company, but it tires him."

That evening Grandpa called me to his room before he went to sleep. "Tomorrow," he said, "when you come home, it will be time to give you the medicine bag."

I felt a hard squeeze from where my heart is supposed to be and was scared, but I answered, "OK, Grandpa."

All night I had weird dreams about thunder and lightning on a high hill. From a distance I heard the slow beat of a drum. When I woke up in the morning, I felt as if I hadn't slept at all. At school it seemed as if the day would never end and, when it finally did, I ran home.

Grandpa was in his room, sitting on the bed. The shades were down, and the place was dim and cool. I sat on the floor in front of Grandpa, but he didn't even look at me. After what seemed a long time he spoke.

"I sent your mother and sister away. What you will hear today is only for a man's ears. What you will receive is only for a man's hands." He fell silent, and I felt shivers down my back.

"My father in his early manhood," Grandpa began, "made a vision quest to find a spirit guide for his life. You cannot understand how it was in that time, when the great Teton Sioux were first made to stay on the reservation. There was a strong need for guidance from *Wakantanka*,[8] the Great Spirit. But too many of the young men were

8. *Wakantanka* [wä kän′ tänk ä]: Great Spirit, creator of the world.

Medicine Pouch Sioux, late nineteenth century, 6 cm, Robert Hull Fleming Museum at the University of Vermont, Read Collection

Red Cloud Oglala Sioux Edward Curtis, 1905, black-and-white photograph, Philadelphia Museum of Art

filled with despair and hatred. They thought it was hopeless to search for a vision when the glorious life was gone and only the hated confines of a reservation lay ahead. But my father held to the old ways.

"He carefully prepared for his quest with a purifying sweat bath, and then he went alone to a high butte top[9] to fast and pray. After three days he received his sacred dream—in which he found, after long searching, the white man's iron. He did not understand his vision of finding something belonging to the white people, for in that time they were the enemy. When he came down from the butte to cleanse himself at the stream below, he found the remains of a campfire and the broken shell of an iron kettle. This was a sign that reinforced his dream. He took a piece of the iron for his medicine bag, which he had made of elk skin years before, to prepare for his quest.

"He returned to his village, where he told his dream to the wise old men of the tribe. They gave him the name *Iron Shell*, but neither did they understand the meaning of the dream. This first Iron Shell

9. **butte top** [byüt top]: top of a steep, flat-topped hill.

kept the piece of iron with him at all times and believed it gave him protection from the evils of those unhappy days.

"Then a terrible thing happened to Iron Shell. He and several other young men were taken from their homes by the soldiers and sent far away to a white man's boarding school. He was angry and lonesome for his parents and the young girl he had wed before he was taken away. At first Iron Shell resisted the teacher's attempts to change him, and he did not try to learn. One day it was his turn to work in the school's blacksmith shop. As he walked into the place, he knew that his medicine had brought him there to learn and work with the white man's iron.

"Iron Shell became a blacksmith and worked at the trade when he returned to the reservation. All of his life he treasured the medicine bag. When he was old, and I was a man, he gave it to me, for no one made the vision quest any more."

Grandpa quit talking, and I stared in disbelief as he covered his face with his hands. His shoulders were shaking with quiet sobs, and I looked away until he began to speak again.

"I kept the bag until my son, your mother's father, was a man and had to leave us to fight in the war across the ocean. I gave him the bag, for I believed it would protect him in battle, but he did not take it with him. He was afraid that he would lose it. He died in a faraway place."

Again Grandpa was still, and I felt his grief around me.

"My son," he went on after clearing his throat, "had only a daughter, and it is not proper for her to know of these things."

He unbuttoned his shirt, pulled out the leather pouch, and lifted it over his head. He held it in his hand, turning it over and over as if memorizing how it looked.

"In the bag," he said as he opened it and removed two objects, "is the broken shell of the iron kettle, a pebble from the butte, and a piece of the sacred sage."[10] He held the pouch upside down and dust drifted down.

"After the bag is yours you must put a piece of prairie sage within and never open it again until you pass it on to your son." He replaced the pebble and the piece of iron, and tied the bag.

10. **sage** [sāj]: a small shrub whose leaves are used as seasoning and in medicine.

I stood up, somehow knowing I should. Grandpa slowly rose from the bed and stood upright in front of me holding the bag before my face. I closed my eyes and waited for him to slip it over my head. But he spoke.

"No, you need not wear it." He placed the soft leather bag in my right hand and closed my other hand over it. "It would not be right to wear it in this time and place where no one will understand. Put it safely away until you are again on the reservation. Wear it then, when you replace the sacred sage."

Grandpa turned and sat again on the bed. Wearily he leaned his head against the pillow. "Go," he said. "I will sleep now."

"Thank you, Grandpa," I said softly and left with the bag in my hands.

That night Mom and Dad took Grandpa to the hospital. Two weeks later I stood alone on the lonely prairie of the reservation and put the sacred sage in my medicine bag.

VIRGINIA DRIVING HAWK SNEVE

Virginia Driving Hawk Sneve was born in 1933 in Rosebud, South Dakota, and grew up on the Sioux Reservation there. She has spent most of her life in her native state, teaching English and speech, and writing about Sioux life and legends. Sneve has said, "In my writing . . . I try to present an accurate portrayal of American Indian life as I have known it. I also attempt to interpret history from the viewpoint of the American Indian and in so doing I hope to correct many misconceptions and untruths. . . ." "The Medicine Bag" is from her book titled *High Elk's Treasure*. Some of her other books include *Jimmy Yellow Hawk* and *When the Thunder Spoke*.

Randy: My Whole

from Putting It All Together

EDITED BY PAULA McGUIRE

Family Is Women

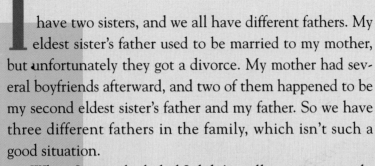

I have two sisters, and we all have different fathers. My eldest sister's father used to be married to my mother, but unfortunately they got a divorce. My mother had several boyfriends afterward, and two of them happened to be my second eldest sister's father and my father. So we have three different fathers in the family, which isn't such a good situation.

When I was a little kid I didn't really notice it much; my mind was on playing and having fun. Back then, I just had a mother, and I thought that was all I was supposed to have. Mom took care of me and my sisters. Everybody was happy. My mother didn't say much about my father. She didn't explain why there was no one there, and I never really asked. My sisters probably knew, but they never told me, and I never talked to them about it. We were happy, just Mom and my sisters.

Not having a father really struck me during my junior high school years. All of a sudden everybody started talking about my dad this, my dad that. I just sat down one day and said, "Where's my father? What's he doing for me?" I really got a complex about it. I felt depressed and angry. Sometimes my friends would talk about their dads, and I'd just blow up at them. Jealousy, I guess. But it was tough.

Ever since I can remember, my sisters have been going off to see their dads, or their fathers would come to the house and visit them. And that, too, contributed to my jealousy. I'd think, "God, they get to see their pops.

I don't get to see mine." I didn't hate them, but I sure felt they were more lucky than I was. They still see their fathers and go to visit them. But all this time, there has never been any talk about my father or any explanation for the situation.

My sisters are grown up now and married. We came out pretty well, actually, when you think about it. I think a lot of people would be pretty down under without a father, but I came through all right.

But when I first noticed it, it crushed me. It struck me all of a sudden. Other kids would say, my father's a lawyer, my dad goes overseas and does this, my father's a professor at the university. I had to lie about my father. I said he was a car dealer. It was tough. It hurt. I had to work it out. I looked at myself and said, "Hey, I'm talented, I'm attractive, I have the smarts. Some people have fathers but they don't have that, so I'll just make the best of it. If it wasn't supposed to be this way, God would have made it different. But God made it this way, so I'll just have to blossom the way I'm planted."

My whole family is women. I look back in the past, and every lady in my family never really had a man. They were married, but it didn't work out. They're all manless. My grandmother doesn't have a husband, my great-grandmother doesn't have a husband, my aunts don't have husbands. But all the women are great.

My mother is a dietician, so she's got a pretty good job and has been able to carry us along. It's been tough, though, believe me. We've all had to work.

I was always pretty worried about my mother too. My mother didn't show much emotion, but I know down deep inside she was probably hurting. I can look in her eyes every day, I can look in my grandmother's eyes every day, and you can tell it's been tough on them. But they're strong now, and they know they have to make it, so there's no sense really being down about the situation when it's not going to help.

I know my mom missed having a husband, having a partner to help out. She needs companionship. She has boyfriends, and I can see they make her happy. Once she laid down little hints to me that she was thinking about getting married. I objected. I didn't say, "No, Mom, don't get married," but I let her know I wouldn't really approve of it. I got jealous. I'd been the male figure in the family, and for somebody to invade my space—that was terrible. I was selfish, but I was very young then. I didn't cooperate at all. I'm sorry now.

I wouldn't say the same thing now. I would encourage her to get married. In fact she has one good boyfriend now, and he likes me. He's a real nice guy and he's helped me a lot. So whatever she wants to do. As long as she's happy. I want to see my mom happy.

I've seen my father before, but I haven't seen him in a long time. I don't think I will, unless I go to see him. I hope I will. I don't hate him. You might think that's funny, but I don't hate him. Hey, I love him! I'll be honest with you, my father's my father. My life has been tough, but there have been a lot of great things. A lot of great people. If it wasn't for him I wouldn't be here. I'll give him that much credit.

What does really burn me up, however, is that he has another family. Actually I have another brother and sister. I feel kind of jealous, and I feel bad for my mother. He's over in R____ , living it up with a wife and a nice family and stuff, and he leaves me with my mother. Put the burden on my mother. But I put myself where I can look at him and say, "Hey, you're not really a man. You going and leaving my mother like this, you're not really a man. And I want to be better than you." So I will. I'm going to be the man in my family that all the women deserved but never got. I'm going to represent that man!

I used to dream what it would be like to have a father. I had all these funny thoughts; it'd be great, we'd go fishing, play sports and stuff. Every day I looked at my friends and thought, they're probably having all that fun. And I'm not having it. They'd talk about what they did with their dads, and I couldn't do that. I was so jealous. Nobody talks about their mom. [Laughs.] I did though, 'cause I had to!

That's another thing, success is very important in this town. Most of the people around me are in successful families with successful fathers. I used to feel pretty inferior around those people. Wealth is important around here. Compared to those people, I'm not so wealthy. I don't live in such a nice area of town. Other people around here talk about going yachting, going skiing in Vermont, and so forth. My mom goes out and breaks her back so I can have some dinner to eat!

That's why I want to be a father. That's my goal, just to be a *good* father. How could you leave a lady anyway? I mean, if it doesn't work out, okay, but at least come back and visit the children.

When I was going through that bad time in junior high, there were so many changes in my life going on—physical, social—I just got caught up in them. I didn't know what to do and had to rely on my own self to carry through. It would have helped to have someone. I wanted a brother too. I grew up with just girls, girls, girls. I needed a male figure just to talk to, just to be with. On the other hand, being with *ladies* has helped me. Because I'm more sensitive now. I care about other people's feelings. I'm not the macho man who tells a woman what to do. I see the woman's side of things. So that's helped me become a more full person. That's why I'm good with girls now. Because I understand.

But for a while, I couldn't do anything. I didn't play basketball for a couple of years. I didn't have much confidence in myself. And I think all that could be linked to my feeling bad about not having a father, about not having anybody to support me. You know, when you're down you talk to your mom or your pop. And I didn't want to talk to my mom, because I didn't want to put any more burdens on her. So usually I'd solve my problems by myself. But maybe during this time in my life I really needed somebody to turn to. But nobody was there. My sisters were in school, and I couldn't talk to friends about that. At least not then.

I wish I hadn't held it all in, but during that time I was feeling too unsure about a lot of things. And up until that point, my life was great! I was a good athlete, pretty good student, I had good friends, both black and white. Then all of a sudden, I don't know, I just thought that I couldn't do it any more. I didn't have anybody there for me. So I got lost in myself. I wasted away. I just got lazy and didn't do anything for myself.

Anyway, I'm back on the track now. I just seem to have this ability to come through. It's natural. I don't want to go into detail about this, but I think my situation was made to be. God put me on earth for a purpose. Because nobody in my family had a father. At least a man who stays around. So I was put on the earth as a very talented young man, attractive young man, I think, very intelligent, to compensate for what I didn't have. I always had this air about me that attracted people. I could do a lot for myself without even trying. Things came easy. Things besides family life. You put aside all the financial burdens and all the family burdens, things were pretty easy for me. That really never stopped. The only thing that ever stopped me was *me*. And I did stop myself for a while, but that's over with. I've been humbled, and I know now.

Would I want to have had it some other way? No, I'm not going to say that. No, I'm happy. If that's the way it is, that's the way it is. I'm not going to say I wish it had been different.

It hasn't been easy, but I've been able to cope. Other kids have had it worse. I can remember kids coming to school, saying their parents were getting a divorce, and looking really bad, being in really bad shape. Maybe they had lived with their father and mother for ten or fifteen years, and all of a sudden there's a divorce. That can be emotionally very hard. Very depressing. But me, I never had a father to begin with, so you can't miss what you've never had.

But if I was to talk to my father now, I'd let him know something. I wouldn't be *that* friendly with him or anything. I'd just let him know that "Hey, I don't hate you or anything. I don't particularly like you for what you did, but you're still my father, and you have to live with that." I will. I'll go to see him, maybe next year when I get my navy uniform. That'll shock him. "This is ME, man!" I'll say. "I'm your son, man. Mom and I did without you, man!"

Asking Big Questions About the Literature

What kinds of changes do people experience?

MAKE

AN OVERVIEW CHART

Make a chart of the changes experienced by the characters in this unit. In the column headed *Change(s)*, list changes that happen to the character. Label these *E* for *external*. Also include changes that happen within the person. Label these *I* for *internal*. A chart has been begun for you in the right column. When you have finished, compare your chart with others in your class. Notice the different ways classmates interpreted changes.

Literature	Character	Change(s)
"As It Is with Strangers"	Tiffany	1. Discovers she has a half brother. *E* 2. Discovers new inner strengths. *I* 3.

Write a

GREETING CARD

Create a greeting card for a friend who has recently experienced a change, or do the same for a character in this unit. Identify the change on the outside of the card. On the inside, write a greeting to congratulate this person or to make him or her feel better. Use your imagination and create illustrations for the card.

LITERATURE STUDY

Characterization

Sometimes actions speak louder than words. Revealing a character's traits through his or her actions is one aspect of **characterization**—the way in which a writer makes a character come alive.

Write the name of a character in the literature whose actions make him or her seem lifelike. Then write a paragraph describing what character trait a specific action reveals to you. For example, in the beginning of "The Banana Tree," James Berry tells us that "the eldest boy, Gustus, sat farthest from his father." What does this tell you about Gustus's feelings toward his father? (*See "Characterization" on page 118.*)

What challenges result from these changes?

Writing a
SONG

Team up with a classmate to write a song (or poem) about one of the challenges experienced by a character in this unit. Make sure your music and song lyrics convey a strong, positive message that will help other young people deal with a similar challenge.

LITERATURE STUDY
Conflict

Have you ever talked to yourself? If you have, don't worry. You were probably hashing over a challenge or a problem you were facing. In this kind of **conflict**, the forces at odds are within yourself.

When a character in literature talks to himself or herself, that conversation is called a monologue. Write a monologue for one of the characters in this unit. Show the internal conflict that the character is experiencing. (*See "Conflict" on page 119.*)

F.A.C.E.
THE CHALLENGE

As producer of a television program entitled "Face the Challenge," it's up to you to find stories about people and the challenges they face. Write a memo to your supervisor urging that the network do a story about one of the characters in this unit. In your memo, include details that illustrate the character's challenge. A memo has been started for you.

To:

From:

Subject: Proposal for an episode of "Face the Challenge"

Date:

Please consider using Martin from "The Medicine Bag" as the star of an episode of "Face the Challenge." I am convinced that he is a good candidate because . . .

Asking Big Questions About the Literature

What choices do people make when faced with challenges?

Create A RADIO TALK SHOW

With several classmates, create a call-in radio talk show. Some members of your group will portray characters in this unit who call to ask questions about challenges they face. For example, the father in "The Writer" might ask: "How can I protect my daughter from hurt as she gets older?"

Other group members will act as a panel of experts who answer questions. Create a catchy title that reflects the show's content and appeals to the audience most likely to tune in.

Write an
ADVICE COLUMN

Write an advice column to help one character in *Changes and Choices* make a different choice from the one he or she made in the story. Make a cluster or web like the one shown to help you gather ideas. Use advice columns in magazines and newspapers as models.

LITERATURE STUDY

Conflict

Have you ever heard the expression "No pain, no gain"? When people face change, they often experience pain or conflict. In literature, a **conflict** is the struggle between opposing forces.

Conflict is internal when it comes from within a person, such as a conflict of conscience. Conflict is external when it occurs between two people or between a person and the outside world.

Choose a character from this unit and identify the type of conflict he or she faces. Write a paragraph explaining what the conflict is. Use specific examples from the selection to defend your choice. (*See "Conflict" on page 119.*)

Reveals fears to his mother when invitation arrives

Talks to other friends who may have the same fears

Harry

What qualities help people face change successfully?

COMPARE & CONTRAST

Which two characters from different stories in *Changes and Choices* might be good friends in real life? Draw a Venn diagram, as shown, in which you compare and contrast these two characters. In addition to listing qualities that help these characters face challenge, include details about their lives, such as age, gender, and neighborhood.

Harry from
"The Torn Invitation"

Martin from
"The Medicine Bag"

Parents born
in a foreign
country

Lives with
mother and
father

Loves
someone
dearly but
feels
ashamed
of that
person

Grandfather is
Native
American

Lives with
mother, father,
sister, and,
eventually,
grandfather

LITERATURE STUDY
Characterization

The way in which a writer reveals a character's traits and qualities is called **characterization.**

Suppose a writer wants to let us know that a character is selfish. The writer may reveal this trait directly by saying "Maria is selfish." Or the writer may reveal this trait indirectly by showing us what Maria *does* that shows she is selfish, what Maria or other characters *say* that shows she is selfish, or what Maria *thinks* that shows she is selfish. (*See "Characterization" on page 118.*)

With a partner, agree on a character from this unit to analyze. Write down the character's name and generate a list of traits that describe him or her. Then create trait webs or clusters. In the center of each web, write a trait, such as *selfish*. In the outer portions of the web, show how the writer reveals this trait in the story.

PLAY a Role

Work with a partner to role-play a situation in which you face a personal challenge or crisis, such as the death of a family member or the loss of a good friend. How would you respond? As you role-play, draw upon the qualities that helped characters in this unit successfully face challenge.

NOW *Choose a Project!*

Three projects involving changes and choices are described on the following pages.

Writing Workshop

WEAR A CRITIC'S HAT

Prewriting
GETTING STARTED

Usually people want to see a movie or read a book because they've heard others say how good it is. For this project, *you* will be the reviewer; you'll recommend or pan the work you've chosen. Your **purpose** in this project will be to evaluate or review a movie, a play, a performance, or a book about people who are going through changes and making choices. Your **audience** will be other students or members of your community.

To help you choose a work to evaluate, try freewriting in your journal. Write for three to five minutes without lifting your pen from your paper.

* Don't Forget *
Helen Keller play done
Miss Hoglin's class

* Possibilities for Project *

★ To kill a Mockingbird — ~~Book~~ Book & Movie

★ Gary Soto ➡ what did I read by him?

★ Pieces from this ~~project~~ unit
(Taste of Melon) or another?

★ Book about Richard Wright ← check in library

★ Something with never in title
➡ Story of girl fleeing Cambodia

★ Bio of Bruce Lee, Roger Clemens?

Write down the names of movies or plays you've recently seen, performances you've attended, books or short stories you've read. Choose works that you have strong feelings about, either positive or negative, or works that really affected you. Then circle one work that you'd like to review for classmates or friends.

Prewriting
BEGINNING TO EVALUATE

Look in newspapers or magazines—or even on TV—for reviews done by professional critics. How are these reviews usually set up? Then think about who the audience for your review will be. Will you publish your review in the school or local newspaper? Can you videotape your review, perhaps working with a partner, and show it on your local cable station? Knowing your audience will help you decide what to include in your review and where to present it.

Now consider how you feel about the work you've circled in your journal. Did you like it or not? Why? What changes does the main character experience? What choices does he or she make?

Think about different elements that you noticed. For example, if you review a book, think about elements like plot, setting, and character. If you review a movie, think about elements like plot, acting, music, and special effects.

Judge the strengths and weaknesses of each element. In your journal, rank each element using a chart similar to the one that follows. Give a reason for each rating.

	Poor	Fair		Excellent		Reason for Rating
	1	2	3	4	5	
Taste of Melon				✓		Exciting! Like struggle between right & wrong
				✓		Mr. Wills is great—like how he changes at end
Plot						
Setting						

With both your audience and the strengths and weaknesses of the work you've chosen in mind, you're ready to draft your review.

- To get your audience's attention, write a catchy beginning. For example, Tony Durso, a student writer, asks a question to introduce his review of the short story "The Taste of Melon" on pages 110–111. " How far would <u>you</u> go to gain the acceptance of your friends?" Notice that the rest of Tony's first paragraph includes the title and author of the work and states his judgment of the work.

- Tell why you did or didn't like the work. Make sure to support your judgment with specific details, quotations, and examples from the work. For example, Tony explains that one reason he recommends "The Taste of Melon" is that Mr. Wills is such a strong character. He supports his recommendation by the following quotation about Mr. Wills: "He straightened, a great, strangled cry tearing out of his throat. It chilled me deep down and all the way through, like the cry of a wild animal." You could write a separate paragraph discussing each element from your chart.

- End by summarizing your response to the work. Give it "thumbs up" or "thumbs down" by recommending the work to your audience or telling them why they shouldn't read or see it. Tony ended his review as follows: "Read this story! It proves that good things <u>can</u> grow out of bad experiences."

Keep in mind your purpose—to write a review—and your audience when you write. Use clear, precise language to convey your judgments and opinions. To motivate his audience to read "The Taste of Melon," for instance, Tony wrote comments such as "I really recommend this story" and "Read this story!" Finally, when you write your review, use the present tense.

Revising
YOUR REVIEW

Ask a partner or a group to respond to your review and make suggestions for improving it. Do you state your judgment of the work? Do you tell your audience enough about the work to get them interested? Do you tell them too much? You don't want to give away the ending of a really exciting book, for example. Do you support your judgments with specific details, quotations, and examples from the work that you're reviewing? Have you successfully persuaded your audience either to avoid or to read or see the work you've reviewed?

Look at the model on pages 110–111 for an example of a review.

Editing
YOUR REVIEW

After you've revised your draft, work with a partner to edit your review. Read one another's reviews and check for errors in spelling, grammar, and punctuation. Correct your errors and make a publishable copy of your review.

PROJECT 1 Writing Workshop

Publishing YOUR REVIEW

Now share your review with your audience. Brainstorm creative ideas for publishing and write your ideas in your journal. Here are some ideas to get you started.

- Create a classroom newsletter called the "Critical I" in which you print your own reviews.
- Invent a rating system like the one shown on this page to rank books, movies, and pieces of literature. For example, use a scale of bookmarks to rate books; a real page turner would rate five bookmarks.

STUDENT MODEL

"The Taste of Melon"

review by Tony Durso, Belmont, Massachusetts

How far would <u>you</u> go to gain the acceptance of your friends? In the short story "The Taste of Melon," Borden Deal tells the story of a sixteen-year-old boy who wants to be liked by his friends and will do anything to gain their admiration—even steal. I really recommend this story. It does a great job of showing what happens when you do something wrong.

"The Taste of Melon" is about stealing and what it does to the person who steals. The boy just wants to impress his friends. He's new in town and doesn't really fit in yet. He and his new friends hear about Mr. Wills's huge seed melon and how carefully Mr. Wills guards it, and suddenly the boy decides to steal it.

At first, the boy thinks stealing is fun, and it is. It's fun to sneak into the tall grass, break the stem off, and roll the melon into the creek to safety. It's a thrill to risk being caught by Mr. Wills, who's so close that the boy can see his teeth glistening. It's fun to break the melon open with his friends and eat the sweet fruit. But by the end, the boy is depressed about what he's done and talks about his let-down in the following words: "I did not feel triumph or victory, as I had expected, though I knew that tonight's action had brought me closer to my friends than I had ever been before."

Mr. Wills is my favorite character. At first, everyone thinks he's a sourpuss. The boy is even afraid that Mr. Wills will hurt him. The scene where Mr. Wills realizes the melon is gone is just great. "He straightened, a great, strangled cry tearing out of his throat. It chilled me deep down and all the way through, like the cry of a wild animal."

In the end, though, Mr. Wills turns out to be a pretty nice guy. He smiles when the boy gives him the bag of seeds and says, "I'm sorry." When the boy also says he'll be willing to help Mr. Wills plant the seeds, Mr. Wills says they can grow the seeds together. Read this story! It proves that good things can grow out of bad experiences.

Cooperative Learning

WELCOME TO MIDDLE SCHOOL!

The PROJECT

Do you remember your first day of middle school? What was your biggest challenge? What worries or questions did you have? This project will give you a chance to think about changes you've experienced and choices you've made. With a partner or a group, you'll create an orientation packet for students beginning middle school next year.

The PROCESS

Put yourself in a sixth grader's shoes. Work with a partner or a group to list questions a new sixth grader might have—about teachers, the building, sports teams, and other issues.

Then select the most important questions. Categorize them by sorting the questions into groups, such as *Questions About the Building* or *Questions About Classes*. Add the answers and other helpful information. Don't be afraid to be funny if it's appropriate. Draw maps or illustrations to help orient sixth graders to your school. If you can, use photographs of teachers, the principal, and other school personnel.

In your journal, make a chart like the one below to keep track of what tasks you must do, which member of your group will do each task, and what materials you and your group will need.

Task	Materials	Person Responsible
Brainstorm questions		
Categorize questions		
Answer questions		
Create graphic aids		

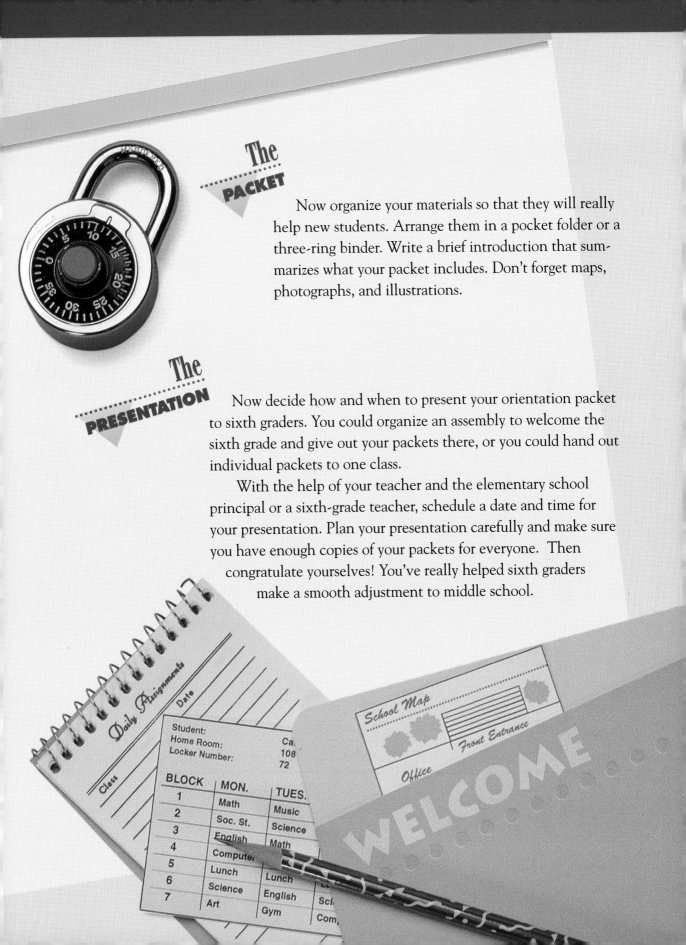

The PACKET

Now organize your materials so that they will really help new students. Arrange them in a pocket folder or a three-ring binder. Write a brief introduction that summarizes what your packet includes. Don't forget maps, photographs, and illustrations.

The PRESENTATION

Now decide how and when to present your orientation packet to sixth graders. You could organize an assembly to welcome the sixth grade and give out your packets there, or you could hand out individual packets to one class.

With the help of your teacher and the elementary school principal or a sixth-grade teacher, schedule a date and time for your presentation. Plan your presentation carefully and make sure you have enough copies of your packets for everyone. Then congratulate yourselves! You've really helped sixth graders make a smooth adjustment to middle school.

Daily Assignments

Date

Class

Student:
Home Room:
Locker Number:

Ca
108
72

BLOCK	MON.	TUES.
1	Math	Music
2	Soc. St.	Science
3	English	Math
4	Computer	
5	Lunch	Lunch
6	Science	English
7	Art	Gym
		Com

School Map

Front Entrance

Office

WELCOME

PROJECT 3

Helping Your Community

VOICES FROM THE PAST

Choosing THE PERSON

One of the Big Questions in this unit asks, "What kinds of changes do people experience?" This project will give you a chance to interview an adult—a parent, a neighbor, a family member, or a resident of a nursing home in your community—to find out about changes and choices in his or her life. Your interview will become part of a community oral history project.

Organizing THE INTERVIEW

In your journal, brainstorm a list of people you'd like to interview. Then circle the name of the person you find most interesting. Write a list of questions you'd like to ask your interview subject about changes and choices, using *who? what? where? when? why?* and *how?* to get started.

Now choose a convenient time and place for conducting your interview. Explain the purpose of your project and tell your interview subject that you'll be recording the entire conversation. Before the day of your interview, be sure that you have access to recording equipment—a tape recorder, a microphone, blank cassette tapes—and that you know how to use it.

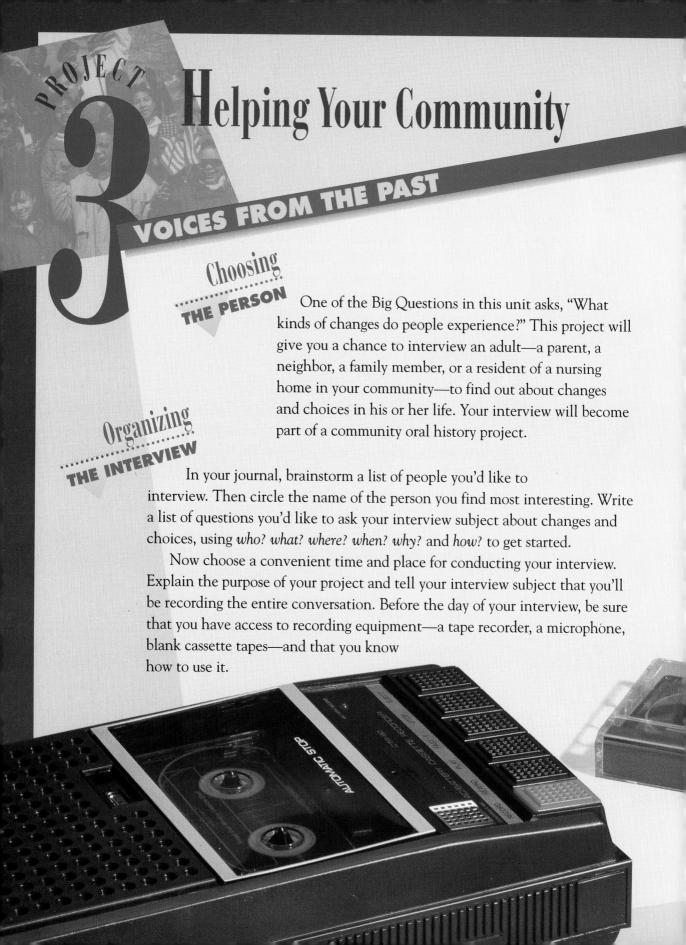

Recording
THE INTERVIEW

On the day of your interview, be sure that your equipment is working properly and that you have a completed list of questions. When you conduct your interview, speak clearly and slowly. Don't worry if you don't get to ask every question you've prepared. Your interview will be more interesting if you let your subject go where your questions lead him or her. When you're finished with the interview, label and date your tape.

Making
AN ORAL HISTORY

After you've recorded your interview, make a label or a J-card for your tape. Identify the interview subject and summarize the interview. Then work with your classmates to do an oral history project. Categorize all the interviews by grouping them according to the changes and choices your interview subjects discuss. Make an index using the following model.

Tape #	Date	Person	Change/Choice	Length
1	4/2	Emma Tewskbury	moved to a new town	20 min
2	4/6	Geraldo Rodriquez	decided to be a doctor	18 min
3				

Presenting
THE ORAL HISTORY

Brainstorm some ideas for presenting your completed oral history project. For example, make copies for the local historical society or the town library. Provide an attractive container for storing the tapes. Notify your local newspaper that the tapes are available to all citizens in your community.

Putting It All Together

What Have You Learned About Changes and Choices?

Now that you've finished *Changes and Choices*, think about how your ideas about this theme have changed. Look back at the writing you've done for this unit—in your journal, in response to your reading, in the Writing Workshop. Share your thoughts with your classmates by writing an essay, a short story, or a poem about a person who has made a choice when faced with a change. Then create your own *Changes and Choices* magazine by collecting the writing you and your classmates have done.

PEOPLE, CHANGES, CHOICES

Prewriting and Drafting Brainstorm a list of people you know or have read about— including characters in this unit—who made admirable choices when faced with challenges. For example, in the 1960s, civil rights activist Rosa Parks, an African American woman, protested against racial segregation by refusing to move to the back of a bus. Choose your favorite person from the list.

Now draft an essay, a short story, or a poem about the person you've chosen. Identify the person and what he or she did. Include facts, quotations, or appropriate funny stories, and provide specific details about this person's changes and choices. Use chronological order (*first, next, last*) to tell what happened, and explain why this person interests you. End with an interesting quotation, a question, or an anecdote.

Revising and Editing It's time to work with a partner. Read your writing aloud to one another. Ask your partner to suggest improvements to the content of your writing. Check the grammar, punctuation, and spelling too.

Publishing Now put your magazine together. Think of an appropriate title and decide on the order of your essays, short stories, and poems. Then design an exciting cover. Share your magazine by displaying copies in your school or local library.

Evaluating Your Work

Think Back About the Big Questions

With a partner, discuss the Big Questions on pages 10-11 and the questions you generated for **Now Think!** on page 11. Do you have trouble answering any of these questions now? In your journal, write two or three sentences discussing how your responses to the Big Questions have changed after your work in this unit.

Think Back About Your Work

Now think about the unit you've just finished and evaluate your work, including your reading, your writing, your activities, and your projects. Be kind to yourself, but be honest too!

Write a note to your teacher. In your note, explain what you've done during this unit and what you've learned. Use the following questions to help you write your note.

- Which literature selections in this unit affected you most strongly? Why?
- What was your favorite activity in this unit? Why?
- What was your least favorite activity? Why?
- If you were to do your project again, what parts would you do the same way?
- What parts would you do differently?
- What did you learn as you worked on your project?
- What have you learned in this unit about what you like to read?
- How would you rate your work in this unit? Use the following scale and give at least three reasons for your rating.

    1 = Outstanding   3 = Fair
    2 = Good   4 = Not as good as it could have been

CHARACTERIZATION

What Is Characterization?

Characterization consists of all the methods a writer uses to create a character who seems like a real person. Such characterization may consist of direct description, or it may be an indirect revelation of the character through dialogue, through what other characters say about him or her, or through examples of the character's appearance and actions. A character who seems so real that readers or audiences feel as though they know him or her in the way that they might know a real person is a *rounded character*. A character who seems to represent an idea, or who seems to have only one main quality, is a *two-dimensional* or a *flat character*.

Writing a Word Portrait Try your own hand at the fiction-writer's craft. Find your favorite character in a selection from this unit. Then imagine this character in an ordinary situation, doing something that involves talking, such as talking on the phone or talking to a friend at a party. Write a detailed, convincing characterization of the person doing this activity, without naming him or her. Finally, see whether a classmate can guess what character you have portrayed.

Creating Real People Write a one-act play, or one scene from a longer play, in which you show who two human characters are through their dialogue and actions. The characters may be based on real or imaginary people, but anyone reading or watching the scene should believe they know both characters well. The setting and plot events are up to you. When your play or scene is finished, invite a friend to take the part of one character as you take the other. Then discuss the characterization with your partner. Is it convincing? If not, revise your manuscript. Then ask your friend to help you present your dramatic work as a reader's theater event for your class.

What Is Conflict?

Conflict in a piece of literature is the struggle between opposing forces. Sometimes the conflict is *internal*, as when the struggle takes place within a person. At other times, for example, when a character struggles against nature, another person, or society, the conflict is external. In drama and narrative fiction, the plot shows how this conflict builds to a point of greatest intensity or interest and is eventually resolved. Most of the reader's interest in the story is really an interest in how the story's conflict affects the main character's life, together with a curiosity about how he or she will resolve the conflict.

Rewriting the Ending Alone or with a partner, choose one of the selections in this unit and imagine a different outcome to the conflict. Then role-play or rewrite the conclusion to show your ideas. Which conclusion do you think works best? Which seems most like real life? Write or talk about why you think so.

Working Out a Conflict Think about the different kinds of conflict in the selections in this unit and how each is developed and resolved. Then, with a partner, discuss a challenging real-life conflict you can imagine yourselves in. It could be a misunderstanding between a parent and a teenager, or the experience of two enemies who find themselves together in a dangerous situation, or two friends debating whether to include a new kid in a group event. What would each person be thinking? How would each show his or her inner thoughts and feelings? With your partner, role-play how the two people become aware of the conflict and gradually work through it. Offer to act out your scene in front of the class.

GLOSSARY OF LITERARY TERMS

A

alliteration   Repetition of the first sound—usually a consonant sound—in several words of a sentence or a line of poetry.

allusion   An author's indirect reference to someone or something that is presumed to be familiar to the reader.

anecdote   A short narrative about an interesting or a humorous event, usually in the life of a person.

antagonist   The person or force opposing the protagonist, or main character in a literary work. [See also *protagonist*.]

autobiography   A person's written account of his or her own life.

B

ballad   A poem, often a song, that tells a story in simple verse.

biography   An account of a person's life, written by another person.

blank verse   Unrhymed poetry.

C

character   A person or an animal that participates in the action of a work of literature. A *dynamic character* is one whose thoughts, feelings, and actions are changeable and lifelike; a *static character* always remains the same. [See also *protagonist, antagonist*.]

characterization   The creation of characters through the characters' use of language and through descriptions of their appearance, thoughts, emotions, and actions. [See also *character*.]

chronology   An arrangement of events in the order in which they happen.

cliché   An overused expression that is trite rather than meaningful.

climax   The highest point of tension in the plot of a work of literature. [See also *plot*.]

comedy   An amusing play that has a happy ending.

conclusion   The final part or ending of a piece of literature.

concrete poem   A poem arranged on the page so that its punctuation, letters, and lines make the shape of the subject of the poem.

conflict   A problem that confronts the characters in a piece of literature. The conflict may be *internal* (a character's struggle within himself or herself) or *external* (a character's struggle against nature, another person, or society). [See also *plot*.]

context   The general sense of words that helps readers to understand the meaning of unfamiliar words and phrases in a piece of writing.

D

description   An author's use of words to give the reader or listener a mental picture, an impression, or an understanding of a person, place, thing, event, or idea.

dialect   A form of speech spoken by people in a particular group or geographical region that differs in vocabulary, grammar, and pronunciation from the standard language.

dialogue   The spoken words and conversation of characters in a work of literature.

drama   A play that is performed before an audience according to stage directions and using dialogue. Classical drama has two genres: *tragedy* and *comedy*. Modern drama includes *melodrama, satire, theater of the absurd,* and *pantomime.* [See also *comedy, play,* and *tragedy*.]

dramatic poetry   A play written in the form of poetry.

E

epic   A long narrative poem—written in a formal style and meant to be read aloud—that relates the adventures and experiences of one or more great heroes or heroines.

essay Personal nonfiction writing about a particular subject that is important to the writer.

excerpt A passage from a larger work that has been taken out of its context to be used for a special purpose.

exposition Writing that explains, analyzes, or defines.

extended metaphor An elaborately drawn out metaphor. [See also *metaphor*.]

F

fable A short, simple story whose purpose is to teach a lesson, usually with animal characters who talk and act like people.

fantasy Imaginative fiction about unrealistic characters, places, and events.

fiction Literature, including the short story and the novel, that tells about imaginary people and events.

figurative language Language used to express ideas through figures of speech: descriptions that aren't meant to be taken literally. Types of figurative language include *simile, metaphor, extended metaphor, hyperbole,* and *personification*.

figure of speech A type of figurative language, not meant to be taken literally, that expresses something in such a way that it brings the thing to life in the reader's or listener's imagination. [See also *figurative language*.]

flashback A break in a story's action that relates a past happening in order to give the reader background information about a present action in the story.

folktale A story that has been passed along from storyteller to storyteller for generations. Kinds of folktales include *tall tales, fairy tales, fables, legends,* and *myths*.

foreshadowing The use of clues to create suspense by giving the reader or audience hints of events to come.

free verse Poetry that has no formal rhyme scheme or metrical pattern.

G

genre A major category of art. The three major literary genres are poetry, prose, and drama.

H

haiku A three-line Japanese verse form. In most haiku, the first and third lines have five syllables, while the second line has seven. The

traditional haiku describes a complicated feeling or thought in simple language through a single image.

hero/heroine The main character in a work of literature. In heroic literature, the hero or heroine is a particularly brave, noble, or clever person whose achievements are unusual and important. [See also *character*.]

heroic age The historical period in western civilization—from about 800 B.C. through A.D. 200—during which most works of heroic literature, such as myths and epics, were created in ancient Greece and Rome.

hubris Arrogance or excessive pride leading to mistakes; the character flaw in a hero of classical tragedy.

hyperbole An obvious exaggeration used for emphasis. [See also *figurative language*.]

I

idiom An expression whose meaning cannot be understood from the ordinary meaning of the words. For example, *It's raining cats and dogs.*

imagery The words and phrases in writing that appeal to the senses of sight, hearing, taste, touch, and smell.

irony An effect created by a sharp contrast between what is expected and what is real. An *ironic twist* in a plot is an event that is the complete opposite of what the characters have been hoping or expecting will happen. An *ironic statement* declares the opposite of the speaker's literal meaning.

J

jargon Words and phrases used by a group of people who share the same profession or special interests in order to refer to technical things or processes with which they are familiar. In general, jargon is any terminology that sounds unclear, overused, or pretentious.

L

legend A famous folktale about heroic actions, passed along by word of mouth from generation to generation. The legend may have begun as a factual account of real people and events but has become mostly or completely fictitious.

limerick A form of light verse, or humorous poetry, written in one five-line stanza with a regular scheme of rhyme and meter.

literature The branch of art that is expressed in written language and includes all written genres.

lyric poem A short poem that expresses personal feelings and thoughts in a musical way. Originally, lyrics were the words of songs that were sung to music played on the lyre, a stringed instrument invented by the ancient Greeks.

M

metamorphosis The transformation of one thing, or being, into another completely different thing or being, such as a caterpillar's change into a butterfly.

metaphor Figurative language in which one thing is said to be another thing. [See also *figurative language*.]

meter The pattern of rhythm in lines of poetry. The most common meter, in poetry written in English, is iambic pentameter, that is, a verse having five metrical feet, each foot of verse having two syllables, an unaccented one followed by an accented one.

mood The feeling or atmosphere that a reader senses while reading or listening to a work of literature.

motivation A character's reasons for doing, thinking, feeling, or saying something. Sometimes an author will make a character's motivation obvious from the beginning. In realistic fiction and drama, however, a character's motivation may be so complicated that the reader discovers it gradually, by studying the character's thoughts, feelings, and behavior.

myth A story, passed along by word of mouth for generations, about the actions of gods and goddesses or superhuman heroes and heroines. Most myths were first told to explain the origins of natural things or to justify the social rules and customs of a particular society.

N

narration The process of telling a story. For both fiction and nonfiction, there are two main kinds of narration, based on whether the story is told from a first-person or third-person point of view. [See also *point of view*.]

narrative poem A poem that tells a story containing the basic literary ingredients of fiction: character, setting, and plot.

narrator The person, or voice, that tells a story. [See also *point of view, voice*.]

nonfiction Prose that is factually true and is about real people, events, and places.

nonstandard English
Versions of English, such as slang and dialects, that use pronunciation, vocabulary, idiomatic expressions, grammar, and punctuation that differ from the accepted "correct" constructions of English.

novel   A long work of narrative prose fiction. A novel contains narration, a setting or settings, characters, dialogue, and a more complicated plot than a short story.

O

onomatopoeia   The technique of using words that imitate the sounds they describe, such as *hiss, buzz,* and *splash.*

oral tradition   Stories, poems, and songs that have been kept alive by being told, recited, and sung by people over many generations. Since the works were not originally written, they often have many different versions.

P

parable   A brief story—similar to a fable, but about people—that describes an ordinary situation and concludes with a short moral or lesson to be learned.

personification   Figurative language in which an animal, an object, or an idea is given human characteristics. [See also *figurative language.*]

persuasion   A type of speech or writing whose purpose is to convince people that something is true or important.

play   A work of dramatic literature written for performance by actors before an audience. In classical or traditional drama, a play is divided into five acts, each containing a number of scenes. Each act represents a distinct phase in the development of the plot. Modern plays often have only one act and one scene.

playwright   The author of a play.

plot   The sequence of actions and events in fiction or drama. A traditional plot has at least three parts: the *rising action*, leading up to a turning point that affects the main character; the *climax*, the turning point or moment of greatest intensity or interest; and the *falling action*, leading away from the conflict, or resolving it.

poetry   Language selected and arranged in order to say something in a compressed or nonliteral way. Modern poetry may or may not use many of the traditional poetic techniques that include *meter, rhyme, alliteration, figurative language, symbolism,* and *specific verse forms.*

point of view   The perspective from which a writer tells a story. *First-person* narrators tell the story from their own point of view, using pronouns such as *I* or *me. Third-person* narrators, using pronouns such as *he, she,* or *them,* may be *omniscient* (knowing everything about all characters), or *limited* (taking the point of view of one character). [See also *narration.*]

propaganda   Information or ideas that may or may not be true, but are spread as though they are true, in order to persuade people to do or believe something.

prose   The ordinary form of written and spoken language used to create fiction, nonfiction, and most drama.

protagonist   The main character of a literary work. [See also *character* and *characterization.*]

R

refrain   A line or group of lines that is repeated, usually at the end of each verse, in a poem or a song.

repetition   The use of the same formal element more than once in a literary work, for emphasis or in order to achieve another desired effect.

resolution   The falling action in fiction or drama,

including all of the developments that follow the climax and show that the story's conflict is over. [See also *plot*.]

rhyme scheme   A repeated pattern of similar sounds, usually found at the ends of lines of poetry or poetic drama.

rhythm   In poetry, the measured recurrence of accented and unaccented syllables in a particular pattern. [See also *meter*.]

S

scene   The time, place, and circumstances of a play or a story. In a play, a scene is a section of an act. [See also *play*.]

science fiction   Fantasy literature set in an imaginary future, with details and situations that are designed to seem scientifically possible.

setting   The time and place of a work of literature.

short story   Narrative prose fiction that is shorter and has a less complicated plot than a novel. A short story contains narration, at least one setting, at least one character, and usually some dialogue.

simile   Figurative language that compares two unlike things, introduced by the words "like" or "as." [See also *figurative language*.]

soliloquy   In a play, a short speech spoken by a single character when he or she is alone on the stage. A soliloquy usually expresses the character's innermost thoughts and feelings, when he or she thinks no other characters can hear.

sonnet   A poem written in one stanza, using fourteen lines of iambic pentameter. [See also *meter*.]

speaker   In poetry, the individual whose voice seems to be speaking the lines. [See also *narration*, *voice*.]

stage directions   The directions, written by the playwright, to tell the director, actors, and theater technicians how a play should be dramatized. Stage directions may specify such things as how the setting should appear in each scene, how the actors should deliver their lines, when the stage curtain should rise and fall, how stage lights should be used, where on the stage the actors should be during the action, and when sound effects should be used.

stanza   A group of lines in poetry set apart by blank lines before and after the group; a poetic verse.

style   The distinctive way in which an author composes a work of literature in written or spoken language.

suspense   An effect created by authors of various types of fiction and drama, especially adventure and mystery, to heighten interest in the story.

symbol   An image, person, place, or thing that is used to express the idea of something else.

T

tall tale   A kind of folk tale, or legend, that exaggerates the characteristics of its hero or heroine.

theme   The main idea or underlying subject of a work of literature.

tone   The attitude that a work of literature expresses to the reader through its style.

tragedy   In classical drama, a tragedy depicts a noble hero or heroine who makes a mistake of judgment that has disastrous consequences.

V

verse   A stanza in a poem. Also, a synonym for poetry as a genre. [See also *stanza*.]

voice   The narrator or the person who relates the action of a piece of literature. [See also *speaker*.]

ACKNOWLEDGMENTS

Grateful acknowledgment is made for permission to reprint the following copyrighted material.

"Growing Up" from *Baseball in April and Other Stories* by Gary Soto, copyright ©1990 by Gary Soto, reprinted by permission of Harcourt Brace Jovanovich, Inc., Publishers.

"As It Is with Strangers" by Susan Beth Pfeffer, copyright ©1989 by Susan Beth Pfeffer, is reprinted from *Connections*, edited by Donald Gallo, by permission of Delacorte Press.

"The Torn Invitation" by Norman Katkov, copyright 1952, copyright renewed 1980 by Norman Katkov, reprinted by permission of the Harold Matson Company.

"The Writer" from *The Mind Reader* by Richard Wilbur, copyright ©1971 by Richard Wilbur, reprinted by permission of Harcourt Brace Jovanovich, Inc., Publishers.

"The Banana Tree" from *A Thief In The Village and Other Stories* by James Berry, copyright ©1987 by James Berry, reprinted by permission of Orchard Books, New York.

"The Taste of Melon" by Borden Deal, published in the *Saturday Evening Post*, September 1985, reprinted by permission of the Borden Deal Family Trust.

"The Medicine Bag" by Virginia Driving Hawk Sneve, published in *Boy's Life*, March 1975, reprinted by permission of the author.

"My Whole Family Is Women" by Randy from *Putting It All Together* by Paula McGuire copyright © 1987 by Visual Education Corporation, reprinted by permission of Delacorte Press.

ILLUSTRATION

67-83 Illustration by Dave Shepherd

PHOTOGRAPHY

4 *l* Nita Winter/The Image Works; **4** *t* Jim Whitmer/Stock Boston; **5** *b* Collection: Museo Rufino Tamayo/INBA Foteca Museo Rufino Tamayo; **6** Sarah Putnam/©D.C. Heath; **8-9** Ken O'Donohue/©D.C. Heath and Company; **10** *t* Carol Palmer; **10** *b* David Strickler/The Image Works; **11** *b* Robert Finken/The Picture Cube; *m* Jim Whitmer/Stock Boston, *t* Jim Whitmer/Stock Boston; **12-13** Tony Savino/The Image Works; **14-15** Frank Cezus/Tony Stone Images; **16-17** Tony Savino/The Image Works; **18-19** Rafael Macia/Photo Researchers; **20** Will McIntyre/Photo Researchers; **22** John E. Fogle/The Picture Cube; **23** Carolyn Soto; **24** The St. Louis Art Museum, gift of Mr. and Mrs. Joseph Pulitzer, Jr.; **28** ©Roy Lichtenstein. Photo by Robert McKeever; **29** Collection of Sydney and Frances Lewis © Roy Lichtenstein; **34** ©Roy Lichtenstein; **35** Photography by Christy Emanuel; **36** ©SEMA, courtesy of the artist; **41** Courtesy of the Museum of African-American Art; **46-47** Museum of Modern Art, New York. Gift of A. Conger Goodyear; **50** Museum of Indian Arts & Culture/Laboratory of Anthropology. Museum of New Mexico, Santa Fe. Cat. 53605/12. Photo by Blair Clark; **51** Courtesy of Norman Katkov; **52-53** David F. Hughes/The Picture Cube; **53** *inset* R. Sorensen & J. Olsen/NHPA; **54-55** Carib Art Gallery, New York City; **58** Collection of the Cummings Family. Photo by M. Lee Fatherree; **63** Courtesy Nohra Haime Gallery, New York; **64** Carib Art Gallery, New York City; **65** James Berry photo; **66-67** Collection: Museo Rufino Tamayo/INBA Fototeca Museo Rufino Tamayo; **70-71** Private Collection, courtesy Samuel Herrup Antiques; **76** The Collection of Mr. and Mrs. Graham Gund; **80-81** Abby Aldrich Rockefeller Folk Art Center, Williamsburg, VA; **83** Babs H. Deal/AP/Wide World Photos; **84** Courtesy Robert Hull Fleming Museum at the University of Vermont; Read Collection. 1881.3.83; **84-85** John A. Anderson Collection. Nebraska State Historical Society; **88-89** Kevin Thomas/©D.C. Heath and Company; **88** *l* The Montclair Art Museum Permanent Collection; **93** *l* Courtesy Robert Hull Fleming Museum, University of Vermont, Burlington, VT.; **93** *r* Philadelphia Museum of Art: Purchased with funds from the American Museum of Photography; **95** *b* Courtesy of Virginia Driving Hawk Sneve; **96** *bl* Myrleen Ferguson/PhotoEdit; **96-97** *b* Bob Daemmrich/The Image Works; **96** *c* Dan Bosler/Tony Stone Images; **96** *cb* Rhoda Sidney/Stock Boston; **96** *cl* Larry Lawfer/The Picture Cube; **96** *cr* Lawrence Migdale/Photo Researchers; **96** *tl* Lawrence Migdale/Stock Boston; **96-97** *t* Julie Houck/Stock Boston; **97** *b* David C. Bitters/The Picture Cube; **97** *c* Bob Daemmrich/Stock Boston; **97** *t* Jose L. Pelaez/The Stock Market; **103** Nancy Sheehan/©D.C. Heath; **106** *b* John Stuart/The Image Bank; **107** Alvin Uptis/The Image Bank; **109** The Far Side cartoon by Gary Larson is reprinted by permission of Chronicle Features, San Francisco, CA. All rights reserved; **112** Jeffry Myers/Stock Boston; **113** *all* Ken O'Donohue/©D.C. Heath and Company; **114** *b* Ken O'Donohue/©D.C. Heath and Company; **114** *t* Rhoda Sidney/Stock Boston; **115** *all* Ken O'Donohue/©D.C. Heath and Company.

Back cover *t/* John Owens/© D.C. Heath: *c,b/* Julie Bidwell/© D.C. Heath

Full Pronunciation Key for Footnoted Words

(Each pronunciation and definition is adapted from *Scott, Foresman Advanced Dictionary* by E.L. Thorndike and Clarence L. Barnhart.)

The pronunciation of each footnoted word is shown just after the word, in this way: **abbreviate** [ə brē′ vē āt]. The letters and signs used are pronounced as in the words below. The mark ′ is placed after a syllable with primary or heavy accent, as in the example above. The mark ′ after a syllable shows a secondary or lighter accent, as in **abbreviation** [ə brē′ vē ā′ shən].

Some words, taken from foreign languages, are spoken with sounds that do not otherwise occur in English. Symbols for these sounds are given in the key as "foreign sounds."

a	hat, cap	j	jam, enjoy	u	cup, butter	**foreign sounds**
ā	age, face	k	kind, seek	u̇	full, put	
ä	father, far	l	land, coal	ü	rule, move	Y as in French *du*.
		m	me, am	v	very, save	Pronounce (ē) with
b	bad, rob	n	no, in	w	will, woman	the lips rounded as
ch	child, much	ng	long, bring	y	young, yet	for (ü).
d	did, red			z	zero, breeze	
		o	hot, rock	zh	measure, seizure	à as in French *ami*.
e	let, best	ō	open, go			Pronounce (ä) with
ē	equal, be	ô	order, all	ə represents:		the lips spread and
ėr	term, learn	oi	oil, voice		a in about	held tense.
		ou	house, out		e in taken	
f	fat, if				i in pencil	œ as in French *peu*.
g	go, bag	p	paper, cup		o in lemon	Pronounce (ā) with the
h	he, how	r	run, try		u in circus	lips rounded as for (ō).
		s	say, yes			
i	it, pin	sh	she, rush			N as in French *bon*.
ī	ice, five	t	tell, it			The N is not pro-
		th	thin, both			nounced, but shows
		ŦH	then, smooth			that the vowel before
						it is nasal.

H as in German *ach*. Pronounce (k) without closing the breath passage.